THE MARSH HARRIER

HAMLYN SPECIES GUIDES

THE MARSH HARRIER

Roger Clarke

HAMLYN

BACK COVER ILLUSTRATION *Adult male Marsh Harrier. Light underwing coverts are a characteristic of maturity.*

First published in 1995 by Hamlyn Limited,
an imprint of Reed Consumer Books Limited
Michelin House, 81 Fulham Road, London SW3 6RB
and Auckland, Melbourne, Singapore and Toronto

Copyright © Reed International Books Limited 1995

Text copyright © Roger Clarke 1995
Colour llustrations copyright © Philip Snow 1995
Black-and-white illustrations copyright © Mark Andrews 1995
Maps copyright © Reed International Books Limited 1995
Photographs copyright © pp. 6, 19, 59 Bennie van den Brink, p.18 and back cover
James White, pp. 42, 43, 46, 47, 58, 82, 83, 90, 94, 98, 115 Roger Clarke

ISBN 0 600 58301 5

A CIP catalogue record for this book is available from the British Library

Page design by Jessica Caws
Maps on pages 35 and 78 drawn by Louise Griffiths
Printed in Hong Kong

CONTENTS

Adult male Marsh Harrier.

Series Editor's Foreword

For the vast majority of ornithologists and birdwatchers, all raptors are rather special birds, and the Marsh Harrier is no exception. Although reasonably common over much of its range, and in some places even seemingly abundant, it is still a relatively rare sight in most of Britain and I always experience a feeling of joy when I see one gliding along low over the marshes or reeds in my home county in coastal southern England, where the species is generally seen only on passage. In contrast to the other European harriers, the males of which are a beautiful grey in colour, both sexes of the Marsh Harrier are much darker, basically brown-looking birds – that is, until one sees them close up. In southern Europe and the Middle East, I have been luck enough to see many Marsh Harriers at very close range, both on migration and during the breeding season, and have marvelled at the subtle contrasts of the adult male's plumage and the bright creamy-buff on the head and forewings of the female. At the same time, the characteristic flight of a harrier, with wings raised in a shallow V as it appears to float effortlessly past the observer, is a marvellous sight to behold.

In most parts of the world, the history of so many birds of prey is one of persistent persecution through prejudice and ignorance. The Marsh Harrier, as a consequence, became extinct in Britain. The fascinating story of its demise and its subsequent comeback detailed within the following pages is a valuable one for the conservationist to read. As Roger Clarke's final chapter shows, however, we cannot afford to be complacent, for our raptors still face many dangers to their future existence, not least of which are the constant threats to their habitats and, in the Mediterranean, the continued illegal shooting of migrating birds of prey (and especially the Marsh Harrier and other low-flying birds). The importance of education and of enforcing existing bird-protection legislation can never be overstated.

Roger Clarke is an acknowledged expert on harriers. In this book, he enthusiastically conveys an enormous amount of information on the reedbed-dwelling Marsh Harrier, including such aspects as its polygynous breeding system, its intriguing hunting behaviour and its impressive aerial displays. His writing, much of it drawn from his own first-hand experience, has certainly taught me much about this species and given me a new insight into its character. The next time I am fortunate enough to encounter a Marsh Harrier in the field, I am sure that the sense of awe these wonderful birds inspire will be even greater.

David A. Christie

Introduction and Acknowledgments

For some time there has been a crying need for one reference source on such a prominent species as the Marsh Harrier. The information, much of it very fine research work and full of interest, has remained scattered throughout the literature, inaccessible to many. Although I am primarily associated with work on the Hen Harrier, I have an equal interest in the other species of the genus and I have collected information on them all on an international basis. I hope that this has given me a wide perspective on the Marsh Harrier. Birdwatching is becoming very much more of an international affair, and although I naturally write from a British perspective, I felt that it would be foolish indeed to restrict the scope of the book to British or European information alone – such a wealth of information has been published on what is essentially the same bird in Australasia and elsewhere. I have tried to bring out interesting aspects of the evolution of members of the Marsh Harrier 'complex' caught in different situations in other parts of the world, which I feel give some insight into the character of the bird. Other sections of the book deal with some personal observations, several with my personal specialization on communal roosting. However, this book is not an account of a detailed personal study, but very much a general review and an attempt to convey the excitement experienced when watching this species in the field.

I wish to thank my friends for their support and for supplying much useful information over the years, especially André Bourgonje who has helped tremendously with translations. I also wish to apologise to those of my family and friends who have suffered, either wittingly or unwittingly, over the past few months during the writing of this book. I am grateful to Jo Hemmings for suggesting this particular title and giving me the chance to write it for Hamlyn and to Cathy Lowne for guiding me through the publication process.

Finally, I should like to share with you the following 1950s book inscription which recently came to my notice: 'To...with the reminder that even one live rabbit, to say nothing of a colony of penguins, is more ecological than any book' (Karl P. Schmidt, Chief Curator, Chicago Museum of Natural History).

1

HARRIERS

Suddenly the bird was there, body slung between two outstretched sails of wings, gently riding the air down out of a cloudless blue wide fenland sky. Long legs dangling with prey in his talons, he was soon over the reed field and his mate was in the air, too. For a few moments they rode parallel until, in a flash of a sideways roll by the female, the food-pass was performed. He had dropped the prey to her talons, and was over the hedge and away. She sailed back down into the reeds of the most secluded field on Wicken Fen. It was a timeless ritual, but this was 1981 and the first year that Marsh Harriers had bred in Cambridgeshire for perhaps a hundred years. I was at the very western edge of the range of a bird that in various forms breeds in suitable habitat east of where I stood, right across Europe, north-west Africa and Asia, and down in Japan, Papua New Guinea, Australia, New Zealand and many small islands in the Pacific Ocean. Isolated forms occur off the east coast of Africa in Réunion, Madagascar and the Comoro Islands. The closely related African Marsh Harrier occupies east and southern Africa.

The Marsh Harrier is that quintessential rarity in lowland Britain: a large and spectacular raptor. Its comeback is one of the major success stories of conservation, if at first a rather private one, confined initially to a few reedbeds in East Anglia. Now, the increasing numbers breeding in Britain have put this 'eagle' of the marshes firmly in the public eye, significantly at the most popular of nature reserves and in the summer season, too. Reserve names such as Minsmere, Walberswick, Hickling, Strumpshaw, Titchwell and Leighton Moss, bywords of birdwatching, just would not have the same ring about them without the Marsh Harrier.

However, our success is not yet complete. The Marsh Harrier is not the most numerous harrier in Britain. In fact, it is one of the rarest of Britain's fifteen species of breeding raptors. Only Montagu's Harrier, the Honey Buzzard and the reintroduced White-tailed Eagle are definitely fewer in number. The strength of the breeding population of the Marsh Harrier is currently on much of a par with those of the Osprey and Red Kite. In the nineteenth century, Britain provided perhaps the most extreme example worldwide of persecution of the Marsh Harrier, which on top of catastrophic habitat loss led to the actual extinction of the species as a breeding bird here at the turn of the century, along with the Osprey, White-tailed Eagle, Goshawk and almost the Red Kite, too. At the time of writing, the Marsh Harrier breeding population of 100–180 pairs stands at about one fifth that of the Hen Harrier. It is true to say that its habitat both is much more restricted than it was hundreds of years ago and will limit the potential of the species in modern Britain. However, I believe that there is still a great

deal more we can do to enable the Marsh Harrier to regain regular successful breeding status in many more counties of Britain than the five or so it has thus far colonized with anything more than one or two nests.

On the world scale, the Marsh Harrier is in many ways the most successful harrier, and one of the world's most successful birds of prey. Its wide distribution covers and extends beyond the ranges of all the other six harrier species in the Old World. Marsh Harriers centre their lives on one of the richest habitats on earth and select their food from the widest possible range of creatures, from crustaceans to mammals. They also carry an intriguing air of duality about themselves. They are obvious, cruising around their marshland habitat, but can also be totally inconspicuous, soaring high in the ecstasy of their spring display, ranging far out over adjacent farmland or settling hidden among the reeds. They are at the same time apparently wayward but deceptively efficient in flight, and are clearly agile enough to catch their fair share of prey. They adopt a resident or migrant strategy. They are threatened, but at the same time small populations are very buoyant at many of the fragmented marshes scattered throughout the Old World. They are brilliant, brightly tricoloured birds in adult male plumage, but otherwise largely plain brown. They are monogamous or polygynous. Almost no other birds can look like such out-and-out ruffians as Marsh Harriers do in the ragged mid-moult plumage of high summer. They are utterly primeval, but totally modern in the glossy pages of today's birdwatching brochures and magazines.

General characteristics of harriers

What physical characteristics make the harriers so special? They are graceful, medium-sized hawks with long wings, long tails and long legs for their body weight, and an effortless, unhurried mastery of the air. Flying generally on stiffly outstretched wings, their outer primaries are 'emarginated' (the width of the web of the end half to two-thirds of the feather is sharply reduced on each side of the shaft) and separate into 'fingers' in flight. They intersperse beating with gliding on wings held raised in a characteristic V shape. As they glide they are easily rocked from side to side by the breeze but their light wing-loading is an adaptation to flying generally low over the terrain for much of the day with relatively little energetic cost. This enables them to search extensively for prey of any type that is of a suitable size and can be suprised on or close to the ground. They are therefore generalist predators rather than specialists on any particular prey. Their distinctive owl-like facial discs betray specialized hearing adaptations which enable them to listen for prey hidden by rank ground vegetation, and their long legs allow them to reach deep into the rank vegetation with their talons. Their cold-searching foraging technique, whereby they tack to and fro low over likely ground, has earned them the name

ABOVE *Montagu's Harriers (left to right) adult male, juvenile and female;* CENTRE *Female and adult male Hen Harriers;* BELOW *Marsh harriers female, sub-adult male and male* 'harrier' for appearing relentlessly to harry their quarry. Likened to the searching by a hound after the scent of its quarry, such hunting is often termed 'quartering'. The technique of surprise they employ involves a low approach masked by structural features of the terrain such as rank vegetation. This means that they must have very fast reactions, since they often encounter prey at close quarters without warning, either for the hunted or the hunter.

Worldwide, the harriers range in weight from the smallest, the male Montagu's Harrier at about 265 g (Nieboer 1973), to the massive female Swamp Harrier in Australasia at about 870 g (Marchant and Higgins 1993). In western Europe, the female Marsh weighs in at about 836 g (Bavoux *et al.* 1988), about three times the weight of the male Montagu's. The difference does not seem quite so great in the field, because of the Montagu's proportionately larger wings and tail, but the range in predation power of the harriers is clearly vast. One glance at the difference in size between the tiny feet of a male Montagu's and the powerful talons of a female Marsh as they stand side by side in a museum cabinet is enough to confirm this.

Apart from the tree-nesting Spotted Harrier of Australia, the harriers are among the few birds of prey habitually to nest and roost on the ground. Perhaps because their flying frame is so finely tuned to open-country living, they rarely use trees to perch, nest or roost in. This would appear to make them vulnerable to predation, but they seem to have evolved senses, such as their remarkable hearing, and behaviours, such as their aerial food-pass and communal roosting, that counter this.

Dimorphism

Among the birds of prey, harriers are a good example of relatively extreme dimorphism, the term used where an animal occurs in two very different forms. In the harriers, dimorphism has both size and plumage dimensions. Female harriers are larger than males. This is an example of 'reversed size dimorphism', or 'RSD' for short. It is termed 'reversed' because the general rule in the animal world is that the male is the larger. The degree of RSD varies from species to species of harrier, with the Hen and Pallid Harriers exhibiting a high degree of RSD for many characters (body weight, wing length, foot size etc.) and Montagu's Harrier a low degree. Hen and Pallid Harriers catch a lot of birds, and Montagu's Harrier takes more lowly prey such as lizards and locusts. This is in accordance with the theory that bird-eating raptors are more highly size-dimorphic. Foot and claw size are probably the best indicators of predation potential. The Marsh Harrier exhibits a medium degree of RSD for a harrier species in these and other characters, reflecting perhaps the smaller amount of agile small passerines in its diet. In the harriers, the degree of RSD is, however, generally greater in foot and claw size than in other characters, enabling the female to kill proportionately larger prey and thereby compensate for her lesser manoeuvrability (Nieboer 1973). Ian Newton (1979) suggests that the raptors pursuing more active prey suffer less competition from other predators and are therefore able to split the prey range of the sexes to occupy a wider niche as a species, and thereby to exploit a larger prey base. Penny and Jerry Olsen (1987) put forward the idea that good providers among males of harriers and other raptors need advanced hunting skills and are a scarce resource to be competed for by females. Larger, stronger females may therefore be at an advantage in competing for mates and will be selected for. A recent theory of Keith Bildstein's (1992) also offers an explanation as to why the size bias should tip towards females rather than males. His 'Head Start Hypothesis' is based on work with the Northern Harrier in the USA. Young male harriers develop faster and fledge earlier. Bildstein reasons that, because males have to provide the majority of the food for female and young, they need to be more proficient at hunting than females. Males appear to achieve this by faster development, but the slower-to-develop sibling female young would be at risk from them if they were not larger in size.

Harriers of the world

The genus *Circus* comprises about eleven species of harrier, inhabiting all of the world's open landscapes except for the interiors of large deserts, the polar ice caps and the tropics in summer. I say *about* eleven because of the uncertainty over the specific status of the several forms of the Marsh Harrier and arguments that the Cinereous Harrier is conspecific with the Northern Harrier. To my thinking, the harriers may be divided broadly into three categories.

Category 1 Highly dimorphic harriers of the northern hemisphere In the first group are four species breeding in the northern hemisphere that exhibit similar extreme dimorphism in the plumages of the sexes. The males of the Hen, Pallid and Montagu's Harriers of Europe and Asia are grey above, with lighter undersides and black wingtips. The females of these species, in brown plumage with white rumps and banded tails, are known as 'ringtails'. So similar are the ringtails that it takes an expert to differentiate between species in the field – using both slight differences in wing shape and action, and subtle differences in plumage. In the Old World, the juvenile Hen Harrier has the same ringtail plumage, but the juveniles of the other two species differ in having plain orange underparts. Pallid and Montagu's Harriers are restricted to the Old World, but the race of the Hen Harrier known as the Northern Harrier is the only harrier in North America, where it has some racial plumage characteristics, including a juvenile plumage more like that of Montagu's and Pallid Harriers with orange underparts and a lack of streaking on the belly. Also breeding in the north, the Pied Harrier of eastern Asia has a striking black, white and grey adult male plumage; the female resembles the ringtails but has more grey in her plumage, and the juvenile is brown with orange underparts. The plumages of the sexes of the harriers in this group are so different that early naturalists understandably mistook males and females for different species. The cryptic ringtail plumage of the females may have evolved as camouflage for nesting on the ground. The light plumage of the males may be an adaptation enhancing their hunting success in open country. It is perhaps significant that their plumage is very similar to that of gulls, which also forage in very open conditions. These harrier plumages have developed in the open regions of the Northern Hemisphere swept by glaciers. A light-coloured underside makes the males less conspicuous against the sky when hunting live prey. It is also a plumage in which the males can show off during their sky-dance courtship displays, their white undersides flashing as they tumble or roll.

Category 2 Harriers of the southern hemisphere The second category consists of five species that breed only in the southern hemisphere. These are the Spotted (Australia), Long-winged and Cinereous (South America), Black (southern Africa) and African Marsh Harriers (southern and east Africa). The plumages of some of these species exhibit little or no sexual dimorphism. Owing to the Cinereous Harrier's resemblance to the Hen Harrier, but with heavy barring on the underparts, Ridgway proposed (late nineteenth century) that it be classed as a subspecies of the Northern Harrier; there are indeed similarities and the idea is mentioned in the modern American handbook, but the two are now treated as separate species. The African Marsh Harrier differs from other Marsh Harriers in its smaller size, lack of sexual plumage dimorphism, monogamy and specialization on mice (Simmons 1991a).

Category 3 The Marsh Harrier complex. The final group is the Marsh Harrier complex or superspecies, excluding the African Marsh Harrier which I have included in category 2 above. These are the largest and most powerful of the harriers. Marsh Harriers are totally absent from the New World, but up to seven forms (or 'allospecies', as constituent species of a superspecies are termed) have been distinguished throughout the Old World. The nominate form is the subject of this book – the Western or Eurasian Marsh Harrier, hereafter referred to in this book as the Marsh Harrier or *aeruginosus*: breeding throughout Europe and in Asia east to about Lake Baikal, it has one recognized subspecies – *harterti*, resident in north-west Africa. In eastern Asia, the Marsh Harrier is replaced by the Eastern Marsh Harrier. Farther south, distinct island forms are found in Papua New Guinea (the Papuan Harrier) and off the east coast of Africa in Réunion (the Réunion Harrier), Madagascar and the Comoro Islands (the Madagascar Harrier). Forms of Marsh Harrier occurring in Australasia are known as Swamp Harriers. The Swamp Harriers in Fiji and many surrounding groups of islands in the Pacific Ocean and those in New Zealand and Australia are very similar. Apart from the Spotted Harrier in Australia, these are the only harriers in this region. Marsh Harriers are very variable in the sexual dimorphism of their plumage, with the male Eastern Marsh being virtually black and white and superficially resembling the male Pied Harrier. The *aeruginosus* male is partly grey, as also are the Australasian males, but much less distinctly so.

2

FIELD RECOGNITION
AND PLUMAGES

Groups of wingbeats interspersed with gliding on stiffly outstretched and raised wings with outer primaries flexing upwards are the hallmarks of harrier flight. The V-shaped outline of a gliding harrier is instantly recognizable. On the glide, harriers are often rocked in the wind and can appear unsteady, but they do clearly cope with this, the result of a light weight-loading and large wings. To increase gliding speed, the harrier partly draws in its wings, angled more sharply at the bend in the forewing ('wrist' or 'carpal joint') and held more on a horizontal plane. The 'fingers' of the outer primaries merge to produce a sharper wingtip. In full soar, the wings are fully extended and pushed a little forward, the fingers splayed and the tail often spread. Hunting low over a reedbed, a typical strike is a characteristic 'roll-pounce' as the bird abruptly checks its progress, spreading its tail and cartwheeling back to dive feet-first on prey. At rest on the ground or on a perch, the tips of the folded wings almost reach the end of the tail.

Gliding on stiffly outstretched wings held upraised in a dihedral or 'V' shape is the basic harrier field character. Even from a great distance, it instantly spells 'harrier'.

The male Marsh Harrier is distinctly different in outline from the heavier female, having slimmer wings and a proportionately longer tail. The leading and trailing edges of the wing are more parallel and the outer wing less tapered than those of other harriers, giving his outline a rather angular feel with fairly blunt wingtips. He is about the same size as the female Hen Harrier. The female Marsh Harrier's body is proportionately larger and the head protrudes slightly more and seems proportionately slimmer than that of the other harriers. The flight is heavier and appears to be slower. The wings are broader, with a clear bulge to the trailing edge of the inner wing caused by longer secondaries and accentuated by a rounding-off towards the body.

Raptors of similar size and dark plumage which might be confused with Marsh Harriers in brown female or juvenile plumage are dark Buzzards, the Black Kite and the dark morph of the Booted Eagle. Buzzards are chunkier and have wider, shorter tails and wider, proportionately shorter wings from the carpal joint outwards. The forked tail when not spread, and the more willowy wing action of the Black Kite contrasts with the stiffer wingbeats and gliding on raised wings of the harrier. The Booted Eagle soars on flat, broader and blunter wings. The Marsh Harrier rests more frequently than the other species of harrier, typically on the ground, perhaps on some slightly raised feature or atop a bush.

The full adult male plumage of the Marsh Harrier is very distinctive and should not lead to any confusion in flight and in adequate light. The pattern from above is tricoloured, with black wingtips (the outer five primaries), a lavender-grey wing-panel (on the inner primaries, primary coverts and all but the innermost secondaries), and the wing-coverts a slanting wedge of the same dark, chestnut or rufous brown as on the back and scapulars. In fact, the brown feathers are edged rufous and wear between moults, resulting in a gradual darkening of the overall tone of brown until the next moult. A yellowish patch or strip on the upper leading edge of the inner wing is a less pronounced version of the female's patagial patches. From below, the wing is white with reddish lesser-streaked and median coverts (they seem to fade with maturity), apart from the black of the outer primaries, which is less extensive from below and does not wedge into the wing as much as from above. The breast is pale with brown streaking, which is heavier lower down and commonly merges into solid rufous on the belly and legs. The head is typically light – cream, yellowish or rusty – with brown shaft-streaks down the centres of the feathers on the crown and nape, varying from narrow to bold depending on the individual. The tail is lavender-grey. Sometimes there is a white patch above the base of the tail, forming a U shape, but usually hardly equivalent to the white rump of other species. The tail-coverts are rufous and coarsely barred on younger individuals, but turn grey with white fringes with age. Close to, the grey of the wings and the tail has a marvellous bloom to it, much as that on a fresh plum and typical of grey harrier plumage.

The hallmark of the adult female's plumage is variability. The ground colour is principally chocolate-brown, more a milk-chocolate colour on the underside and darker on the upperside, wings and mantle. Fresh feathers have a rufous fringe that wears away and, together with fading of the plumage by the sun, make for little of a constant nature in the tone of the brown. The leg feathering is reddish-brown. The tail is brown, but with a rufous marbling on all but the central feathers that is not visible in the field but gives the tail a reddish tone in good light. Examined closely, the marbling on some individuals appears to incorporate the vestiges of barring. Although brown-headed birds do occur, the crown and chin are usually some variant on an orange or yellow tone – cream, primrose-yellow, rusty-yellow, buff – or whitish, depending perhaps on fading and on individual variation, too. Patches similar in colour are normally present on the upperwing-coverts ('patagial patches'), often in a band across the chest, on the mantle, back and sometimes on the underwing and elsewhere, but very variable in extent between individuals. The development of these patches through sub-adult plumage and at older ages is undocumented. Close to, these patches are often clearly variegated yellow and brown, caused by the variable extent of yellow edging to the feathers. Some striking females have large semicircular patagial patches, whilst others have merely a thin strip on the leading edge of the wing. The yellow feathers on the crown and nape have generally narrow brown shaft-streaks, not usually present in the juvenile. The yellow chin is unstreaked. The ear-coverts or 'cheeks' are brown.

Newly fledged juveniles are largely a uniform very dark brown. Most have a ginger crown and often a ginger chin, with brown cheeks. All-dark individuals or individuals with ginger splashes on the forewing and bands on the chest do occur, but less commonly. Buff tips to the greater coverts causing a thin light line on the upperwing are very characteristic of young birds, but soon wear away (similar pale tips are initially present on other feathers, notably the scapulars and tail-coverts). The ginger shade of the head markings soon turns more yellow with a partial post-juvenile moult, involving mainly the feathers on the head and body. There is normally no streaking of the yellow on the crown, but often a brown patch on it, not noticeable at a distance.

Bavoux *et al.* (1991) categorized the characteristics of juvenile plumage as follows, based on 287 birds examined just before fledging. They found no distinction between the sexes in frequency of the specific characteristics.

Crown/nape/neck/back

1 No light patches.
2 A patch on the nape, plain, streaked or scaled brown.
3 A patch extending back from the cere over the crown, sometimes over the nape and infrequently onto the neck and even the back; it can be plain, streaked or scaled brown, and is sometimes divided by a brown blemish on the crown.

Chin/throat

1 No light patch.
2 A patch limited to the chin or extending down onto and around the sides of the throat.

Breast

1 No light patch, sometimes a few 'flame feathers' (rusty-edged with a brown central wedge).
2 A narrow crescent of flame feathers across the breast.
3 A deep crescent of flame feathers.

Upperwing-coverts.

1 No light patch, sometimes a few 'flame feathers'.
2 A small patch of flame feathers on the lesser and median coverts.
3 A large patch of flame feathers extending back to the greater coverts.

The possible combinations of these are of course many, but the plumages occurring most frequently lack patches on the wing-coverts and chest and have patches on the crown and chin/throat, or just a nape patch.

17

In flight, the underwing can be useful to separate adult females and immatures. The impression in the juvenile is of an even shade of dark brown, apart from whitish bases to the primaries whereas the adult female underwing shows a distinct contrast between the more grey-brown secondaries and the sandy-coloured bases to the primaries, which appear to have blackish tips. The underwing-covert feathers on the adult female can have an extensive rusty fringing whereas on the juvenile they are plain dark brown. In the field, however, views of the underwings are not always good enough to permit such simple separation of adult females and juveniles. Juvenile males may be distinguished in flight by their lighter build and narrower wings, especially when side by side with females, but individual variability means that a few individuals of each sex may approach the other in size.

The subadult male plumage has only recently been adequately described, by Clark and Forsman (1990). This is one of the twilight areas of field identification, where males may easily be incorrectly recorded as females. Full adult male plumage is acquired at about two years old, although the colours show less contrast; in particular, the grey is more dingy than on older males and features such as dark tips to the secondaries persist for a time. The grey panels on the upperwing increase in size and grow paler with advancing years (Zuppke 1987). From the time of the post-juvenile moult to the moult at two years, the similarities with female plumage are still great. The distinguishing features are difficult to see in the field. They are a grey cast to many of the feathers in the middle of the upperwing, and a tail with grey central feathers with a dark subterminal band and rufous-brown outer feathers which are often banded. The underwing has variable amounts of whitish mottling or a whitish patch on the secondaries and inner primaries, and where this is extensive it leaves a dark band along the trailing edge of

Dark-headed juveniles are less common than light-headed ones. This one sports some abnormal white feathers in its wings.

Adult female Marsh Harrier.

the underwing. The underwing-coverts and breast can be streaked rufous, or are plain dark brown with a light chest band as on the adult female. To add to the confusion, some adult females can have a silver cast to the tail or faint tail banding. In some cases it is not safe to sex the bird other than by behaviour – seeing it pass prey to a female rising from a nest, for example!

The bill is blackish, the cere greenish-yellow, the gape greenish, legs and feet yellow, and claws black. Eye colour (or, more accurately, iris colour, since the pupil is always dark) begins as dark brown. The traditional wisdom concerning its development is that male irides soon turn light in nestlings and become yellow early in life, whereas those of the female are much slower to change, turning orange and then yellow in older females. A recent study of large numbers of birds trapped by Bavoux *et al.* (1993) in France has, however, demonstrated that the situation is not so clear cut as this. They photographed and categorized the range of eye colours, which included a milky white. It was shown that males are more likely than females to have pale

A number of dark morph Marsh Harriers occur in the breeding population at wetlands in the steppe region of western Asia.

irides after fledging, or acquire them more rapidly, but also that individual variation in the Marsh Harrier makes this a less reliable indicator of sex than in Hen and Montagu's Harriers.

The rare melanistic or dark-morph form of the Marsh Harrier was described by Bill Clark in *British Birds* in 1987, based on migrant harriers caught in Israel for ringing, and on museum specimens. Melanism is also well known in Montagu's and Long-winged Harriers. I had the good fortune to see a dark-morph adult male Marsh Harrier at a wetland in the steppe of the border region of southern Russian and north-west Kazakhstan in June 1993. My lasting impression is of how prominent the bright yellow eye was against such a plumage. The black upperwing-coverts were flecked here and there with white (probably down showing through), and the underwing pattern of black coverts and light bases to the flight feathers was very striking. The male also has a normal grey tail. The female and immature are described as solidly dark brown, with whitish bases to the primaries from underneath and a creamy patch on the nape. I have seen an all-dark female in Slovakia at too great a distance to see these features. Interestingly, Clark hypothesized that most dark morphs come from eastern Europe and western Asia. Anatoly Davygora, who guided me in the steppe, confirmed that perhaps 20 per cent of Marsh Harriers in his region were of the dark form, although I did not personally see any more in ten days of birdwatching. Some have been noted from western Europe, notably France (e.g., Fouquet and Yésou 1991), and in Britain a melanistic male 'very dark but with grey tail and pale patches under the primaries', was seen at Welney on the Ouse Washes in Norfolk on 10 September 1988.

Albinistic or partly white Marsh Harriers do occur. Selby (1825) claimed that 'varieties of this species, with more or less white, are also frequently found', and for several years he kept one in captivity on which 'the throat, bastard wing, the first four quill feathers, and the outer tail feathers, were of a pure white'. In England, in 1989, three nests in Norfolk and three in Suffolk fledged partially white young, and there were several records of such birds in eastern England later that summer. In the same year, a brood of similar birds occurred in Holland, too, and a further such bird was seen elsewhere there (Grootjans and Ouweneel 1990). The sporadic outbreak of partially white birds in one season is remarkable and leads one to speculate whether a temporary environmental factor was responsible. A similar brood occurred in Italy in 1969, photographed by Roberto Parodi. Typically, these birds are very variable in their pied pattern. In Belarus in 1988, Ivanovsky (in Clarke in press a) recorded one young bird with several white primaries and secondaries in one wing. Photographs of the Dutch brood by Bouke Grootjans show great variability in the percentage of white and its distribution among the individuals: one showed broad white bands on the end of the flight and tail feathers and extensively white upperwing-coverts, while another had much less white on the ends of the flight feathers, but white scapulars and greater coverts on the upperwing. Each one photographed seemed to have the normal yellow crown and chin.

Albinism has also been recorded in New Zealand, where one largely white Swamp Harrier was seen flying and behaving normally but, after capture, its white feathers were noted to be more brittle and to wear more markedly than adjacent normally coloured ones. Such birds are very rare, and natural selection must act against them, but survival in the wild seems to be possible since another almost fully albinistic harrier was ringed and was retrapped eight years later (Hedley 1983).

Apart from that of the race *harterti*, of north-west Africa, regional variation in the plumage of the Marsh Harrier has not been seriously claimed, although birds with particularly bold light patches have been said to occur in certain areas, in Romania for example, but this is more likely to be the result of individual variation. The male *harterti* has a darker back and upperwing-coverts, but a paler head with black shaft-streaks (as opposed to brown in *aeruginosus*), lighter underparts which are streaked brown/black and lighter underwing-coverts. The primaries are sometimes barred on the underwing. The female, too, has a plumage with more contrast: very light, almost pure white, head, back and breast patches, and paler rusty-brown underparts.

The Eastern Marsh Harrier is very distinctly different in plumage. The full adult male, boldly patterned black and white, might be described as 'pied' and has indeed been confused with the Pied Harrier from time to time. Perhaps the simplest description is to say that its plumage pattern is similar to that of the *aeruginosus* male, but in monochrome. The face is black, and the crown, nape and breast are heavily streaked blackish on white. The belly and leg feathering is white. The back and upperwing-coverts are mainly blackish with white spots, but the secondaries, inner primaries, primary coverts, alula and tail are light grey. The outer primaries are black, and it has a typically pale leading edge to the wing and a white rump. The plumage of the female is rather intricate, but principally brown with blackish streaking on the body. Greyish flight and tail feathers are barred blackish. She, too, has a white rump. Geographical variation has yet to be sorted out, but males with brown streaking on the head and body and a brown back and upperwing-coverts, intermediate in plumage between *aeruginosus* and Eastern Marsh, do occur, for example in Japan. The plumages of the Réunion, Madagascar and Papuan birds are similar to that of the nominate Eastern Marsh. A melanistic form of the Papuan Harrier is recorded from the highlands, described as a blackish bird with a pale tail and white rump (Coates 1985). Juveniles of these forms are rather similar to *aeruginosus* juveniles.

Farther south, in Australasia, the Swamp Harrier shows markedly less sexual dimorphism in plumage. The male still has grey in the wings and tail, but this is less pronounced than in other Marsh Harriers. The sexes are similar from above, with brown back and upperwing-coverts, grey tail and grey panel on the outer wing (a little more pronounced on the male) and dark primary tips. Both sexes are barred along the wings, and the female across the tail, too, and both have white uppertail-coverts. Below, the base colour is cream, but the adult male can be much lighter, streaked heavily only on the breast, whereas the female is streaked red-brown all the way down the body and on the underwing-coverts. The barring and the white uppertail-coverts are characteristics shared with the ringtail plumage of northern-hemisphere harrier species. Juveniles are a more *aeruginosus*-like uniform dark brown above, with a lighter rump patch and banded tail; below, they are a more red-brown except for the wing, which has blackish secondaries, a very distinctive large light patch at the base of the primaries and blackish primary tips.

The African Marsh Harrier is a little smaller than the Marsh Harrier. The two occur in the same regions in east Africa in winter. The adult male and female African Marsh Harrier are rather similar to each other in plumage. They lack the light-coloured head of the Marsh Harrier and have banded wings and tail, but they are basically brown with a cream patagial patch on the upperwing and cream streaking across the chest; the feathering on the lower belly and legs is very rufous. The juvenile is a dark brown bird with a light patch on the back of the head, and in normal plumage differs from the young Marsh Harrier in having a light chest band and a darker crown.

A light patch, or pair of spots often merging into each other, is present on the back of the head in many harrier plumages. This is called the nuchal or occipital patch or spot and is in fact typical of many hawks. It may have an important function as a signal to a mate or a predator (Hafner and Hafner 1977). Predators cash in on harrier roosts, both owls and mammals such as cats, foxes, wolves and jackals being a hazard at night. In common with many sleeping birds, harriers bury their face into their shoulder feathers, and a light patch on the nape may cause a predator to hesitate as it works out whether it is seeing the face of an alert bird.

3

TAXONOMY, HISTORY AND RESEARCH

Taxonomy

The taxonomic breakdown of the Marsh Harrier complex has been attempted on various criteria – plumage, food specialization, mating systems, display and calls, for example. The unravelling of this taxonomic knot is one of the most exciting and testing challenges of harrier study.

The Marsh Harrier *Circus aeruginosus* (rust/copper-coloured harrier) was named *Falco aeruginosus* by Linnaeus in 1758 (*Systema Naturae*, tenth edition). The genus name Circus was first applied to the harriers in a systematic list by the Frenchman Lacepède (*Mémoirs de l'Institut* iii, p. 506, 1800–01), although the name had appeared in less authoritative works since the sixteenth century. *Circus* is generally deemed to be derived from the Greek word '*kirkos*', meaning a hawk that wheels or flies in circles. The *harterti*

Nineteenth-century collectors hastened the temporary demise of the Marsh Harrier in Britain, but they have left us a legacy of valuable museum material.

race of *aeruginosus* was named by Zedlitz in 1914 after Ernst Hartert, a noted systematist at Tring Museum who was supportive of his discovery. The Eastern Marsh Harrier *C.spilonotus* (spotted-back harrier) was first differentiated in 1850 by J. Kaup in his *monograph of the Falconidae*. The difference in plumage between *aeruginosus* and *spilonotus* is very distinct and is regarded by many as being good grounds for treating the two as different species. Vaurie (1965) believed that there were reasons for regarding them as conspecific, because of interbreeding west of Lake Baikal and in western Mongolia and reports of intermediate individuals in Chinese Turkestan. Reports from recent Lake Baikal expeditions are not exactly clear, but suggest that Marsh Harriers there are not typical *aeruginosus* (both males and females have conspicuous white rumps), and birds there earlier thought to be Pied Harriers may in fact be *spilonotus* (Mlíkovský and Stýblo 1992). Vaurie also noted the similarities between *harterti* and *spilonotus*. The *spilonotus*-like contrast of dark and white in the males and barred brown in the females in the plumages of the Réunion, Madagascar and Papuan Harriers has led to the belief that they are descended from *spilonotus*. This is especially interesting in the case of the Réunion and Madagascar Harriers, because they are located off the east coast of Africa, a long way from the current Asiatic range of *spilonotus*. The theory has been put forward (Nieboer 1973) that *aeruginosus* is a relatively recent development from the *spilonotus* form. This might explain the *spilonotus*-like features in *harterti* plumage and the occurrence of *spilonotus* types isolated on islands off east Africa.

The Cambridge Professor of Zoology and founder with others of the British Ornithologists' Union, Alfred Newton, named and described the Madagascar Harrier *C. macrosceles* (long-legged harrier) at a meeting reported in the *Proceedings of the Zoological Society of London* in 1863. He was working from only two immature specimens collected by his brother Edward, who mounted expeditions to Madagascar during a stint as Assistant Colonial Secretary in Mauritius. The form on Réunion was named *C. maillardi* by the Frenchman Jules Verreaux in 1862, after his colleague L. Maillard, in an appendix to the latter's book *Notes sur l'île de la Réunion*. A superb plate plate of the male and female, again by Wolf, appeared in *Ibis* in 1863 with a note by Philip Sclater, secretary of the Zoological Society of London. *C. spilonotus* was figured in *Ibis* by Wolf in 1863. The similar Papuan Harrier was named *C. spilothorax* (spotted-breast harrier) by Salvadori and Albertis *(Ann. Mus. Civ. Genova 7: 807)* in 1875.

The name *C. approximans* (approximating or resembling [other harriers]) was applied to the Swamp Harrier found in Fiji by the American Peale in an expedition report in 1848. The forms in New Zealand and Australia were subsequently regarded as a race of this bird and were referred to as *C. a. gouldi*. This was a name introduced in 1850 by Bonaparte, nephew of the Emperor Napoleon, after John Gould. Gould had in fact described and figured the bird in his *Birds of Australia* in 1837, but he had mistakenly applied the Spotted Harrier's scientific name to it. The form on New Caledonia was accorded separate specific status for a while by the pioneering bird-of-prey specialist from Norfolk, John Gurney senior, on the basis of subtle plumage differences in specimens examined, and was named *C. wolfi* after the famous wildlife artist of the time, Joseph Wolf. This bird was first illustrated by Wolf in 1865, in the *Proceedings of the London Zoological Society* alongside Gurney's description. The American taxonomist Dean Amadon (1941) found that the Australian form of the Swamp Harrier was slightly larger than the Polynesian birds but did not differ in other characteristics. Checking this more recently, the Australian ornithologist David Baker-Gabb (1979) found no good reason to distinguish between the forms *C. a. gouldi* and *C. a. approximans* in Australia, New Zealand and the Pacific islands on the grounds of size or plumage colour and proposed that they be combined under the name *C. approximans*.

The African Marsh Harrier was named *C. ranivorus* (frog-eating harrier) by the Frenchman Daudin in 1800. Subdivision into the races *C. r. aequatorialis* (East African Marsh Harrier) and *C. r. ranivorus* (Cape Marsh Harrier) has subsequently been adopted by some on the basis that the birds in the east are slightly smaller. Nieboer (1973) considered the African Marsh Harrier to be the least advanced of the Marsh Harriers and therefore possibly the oldest form. The plumages of the Eastern Marsh, Papuan, Réunion and Madagascar and Swamp Harriers all have a number of similarities, and the juvenile plumages of these are so similar as to appear to reveal one root of these forms. In adult male plumage, *aeruginosus* is clearly very different and may well be the result of further and more recent evolution.

The females of the various *spilonotus* and *approximans* forms tend to have barring on the wings and tail and light rumps, reminiscent of ringtails. Males of the *spilonotus* forms also appear to be closer to the extremely dimorphic males of the Hen/Montagu's/Pallid/Pied group. Nieboer (1973) remarked that the Marsh Harriers' male plumage may be less specialized because they do not hunt so much in the open. Instead, the element of surprise comes to the fore in their more closed marshland habitat. The female's plumage may be even less specialized because in reedswamp she is well concealed on the nest by the reeds or similar tall vegetation. The juveniles of all the forms of Marsh Harrier are very similar – dark chocolate-brown, some with light patches on the head. The virtual retention of this plumage by the adult female *aeruginosus* perhaps reflects her lack of a need for cryptic plumage.

Robert Simmons (1991a) made the first tentative comparison of the displays of African, Australasian, European and Réunion Marsh Harriers. He concluded that it was safest to give them all separate specific status on the basis of differences in displays, based mainly on comparison of accounts in the literature. Such accounts are however, open to individual interpretation and are not as satisfactory as data from standardized observations. For example, the 'dropped-leaf' display of the Marsh Harrier is not adequately described in Cramp and Simmons (1980) and is similar to the spiralling descent Simmons describes for the African Marsh Harrier.

Comparison of sonagrams of the display calls of the male *aeruginosus* (Cramp and Simmons 1980), *approximans* (Marchant and Higgins 1993) and *ranivorus* (Simmons 1991a) shows that the patterns, durations (about 0.25 seconds) and frequencies of the calls are very similar except in the case of *ranivorus*, where it is 1 kHz higher-pitched.

In their pioneering work on the taxonomy of the world's birds based on DNA analysis, Sibley and Ahlquist (1991) did not test a range of harriers – only the Northern Harrier against other birds of prey. The species list based on their research (Sibley and Monroe 1991) drew on other work and opinions, and grouped the Papuan Harrier with the Eastern Marsh Harrier and the Réunion Harrier with the Madagascar Harrier. It therefore differentiate five species in the Marsh Harrier complex – the Western (or European), Eastern, African, Swamp and Madagascar Harriers – but Sibley and Monroe commented that a number of the other Marsh Harriers may be conspecific with *aeruginosus*. Further DNA research may well provide the answer.

History from early times to 1900 and extinction in Britain

Willoughby-Vernier reported Neolithic cave paintings in southern Spain capturing the 'jizz' of birds, including the Marsh Harrier. Mummified Marsh Harriers have been found in Egypt dating from 1000 BC (Lortet and Gaillard in Bannerman 1953–63). The only early British harrier records are for the Marsh Harrier, in deposits at Iron Age lake settlements in Somerset (Harrison 1988). The Marsh Harrier was first referred to in print by Turner, in his *Avium Praeciparium* of 1544, the earliest printed bird book. In many respects his words captured the essence of the species. Of the 'Balbushard (Bald Buzzard) of the English' he said, '...with a white patch upon the head, and nearly fuscous in colour, always haunts the banks of rivers, pools, and swamps; it lives by hunting Ducks and those black fowls which Englishmen call Couts. The conflict...between this Eagle...and the water-birds I have seen often, and not I alone, but countless Englishmen witness it daily. If anywhere a little space of ground rises among the reed-beds, there the bird is wont to make a nest, that, since in power of flight it is not very strong, it may not be far distant from its prey. It suddenly attacks birds, and thus takes them. It also sometimes butchers coneys (rabbits)' (translation: Evans 1903).

Vernacular names commonly used by early writers included Bald Buzzard or White-headed Harpy, owing to the light-coloured head in most plumages; Duck Hawk, from its reputation for preying on waterfowl; or Moor Buzzard, from being 'common on heaths and wastes' (Albin 1738) or 'marshy districts and moors' (Selby 1825). The word moor used to be synonymous with a marshy wilderness; the Moorhen, for example, still bears the name. The name Marsh Harrier began to evolve with the use of 'Marsh Hawk' by Edwards in his 1763 *Natural History of Birds* and the 'Hawk' was subsequently changed to 'Harrier' by Selby to group the species with the others of the genus.

'These birds abound in all the marshy districts of England and Scotland' wrote Selby in 1825. In fact, there is no firm evidence that the Marsh Harrier bred at all in Scotland in the nineteenth century (Baxter and Rintoul 1953). In Wales, Montagu (1902) stated that it was 'the most common of the falcon tribe about the sandy flats on the coast of Carmarthenshire, where they prey upon young rabbits; and we have seen no less than nine feeding at one time upon the carcass of a sheep'. More local accounts confirmed that it was plentiful in the right habitat (e.g., Jenyns 1826 for Cambridgeshire). The advance of drainage of land for farming saw much marshy habitat dis-

A male Marsh Harrier tests out a flock of grazing Wigeon for injured individuals. An old name for the species is 'duck hawk', from its reputation for going after shot ducks.

appear in the nineteenth century. Together with persecution by gamekeepers and by nineteenth-century collectors of skins and eggs, the effect on Marsh Harrier numbers was catastrophic. The decline of the species seems to have been swift, reducing it to a prized trophy by the mid 1800s.

Collecting was a very respectable activity of the age. For example, the catalogue of John Wolley's collection of eggs was edited by Alfred Newton, Professor of Zoology at Cambridge, and published in 1864 after Wolley's early death at the age of 36. The few British Marsh Harrier eggs and clutches it lists were mostly from Whittlesea Mere, Huntingdonshire, which was drained in 1851. 'I do not think the Moor Buzzard has bred in the fens of the Bedford Level since the latter date' was Newton's revealing remark. By the late nineteenth century, the ardent Sussex collector Edward Booth was lamenting the difficulties he had encountered in getting to grips with the species, 'considering the time I have spent at all seasons of the year in the neighbourhood of the fens and broads of the eastern counties, as well as in other quarters that are frequented by this species, the observations I have been able to record concerning its habits are scanty in the extreme. The only adults I could ever positively identify were a pair I observed sailing over the reed-beds on Wicken Fen, near Ely'. It is perhaps significant that this was the same spot to which they first returned as breeding birds in Cambridgeshire a hundred years later. For Suffolk, Ticehurst (1932) remarked that he could find no reference to the species breeding for the previous hundred years. The remoter regions of the British Isles appear to have fared little better. In Wales, the last known nests were in Merionethshire in 1869 and 1877 (Forrest 1907). In Ireland, the species was reduced to a few pairs by 1840 and is thought to have eventually ceased breeding by 1917 (Hutchinson 1989). Its last refuge in Britain was in the Norfolk Broads, where single nests were reported (and usually collected) at intervals every few years throughout the late 1800s. The last record is of a nest built in 1899 and photographed by the Kearton brothers, but the adults were trapped (Riviere 1930). By the turn of the century, the Marsh Harrier was, so far as we know, extinct as a breeding bird in Britain.

Comeback and second population crash in Britain, 1900–71

Although Marsh Harriers did summer a few years earlier in Broadland, the first known successful breeding this century was in 1915, at Horsey in the Norfolk Broads, where Lord Lucas, the Hon. Edwin Montagu and Sir Edward Grey were running nearby Hickling as a bird sanctuary. In 1910, permission had been given to them for the wardening of Montagu's Harrier nests on the neighbouring Brayden Marsh, and in 1912 Lord Lucas took over the lease there. In 1915, he came home on leave and hurried down to watch both Montagu's and Marsh Harriers go down to their nests. His words to his head keeper, Jim Vincent, were 'By Jove! Jim, this is the next greatest sight to the War'. He was killed in an aeroplane ascent in Flanders in 1917 and left the properties to Lord Desborough's family for use as a bird sanctuary 'especially for the breeding and preservation of the Harriers'.

The only British breeding records for the next 30 years were from these neighbouring marshes of Hickling and Horsey. Intermittent attempted or successful breeding after 1915 became regular from 1927. Horsey was purchased by Major Anthony Buxton at the beginning of the 1930s. Maintenance of this precarious foothold for the species was due largely to the forbearance and enthusiasm of these landowners in an age when, as Buxton said of harriers, 'nearly everyman's hand is against them'. The story is that he bought the Horsey estate because he saw harriers over the marsh, although the Marsh Harrier ran second to the Montagu's Harrier in his affections. His travels and wider perspective had taught him that 'birds of prey must of course destroy great numbers of other birds, but the supply seems somehow to meet the demand'. Neighbouring estates were not so tolerant. Cock birds sometimes went missing, presumed or found shot. In Buxton's words: 'There appears to be an idea that the harriers are getting too numerous, and even that nothing else can exist in their neighbourhood. The wealth of bird life around them is the best answer to that'.

Buxton's and Vincent's regular notes on harrier happenings, often illustrated by photographs or R.A. Richardson's drawings, were two of the highlights in the county's annual *Wild Bird Protection in Norfolk*, and Buxton continued to write in the first years of its successor, the *Norfolk Bird Report*. This was the golden age of bird photography at the nest and it was encouraged at Horsey; Buxton recognized its value in fostering public interest in natural history. This was important in an age when these birds were so unfamiliar to a public which would have had far more sympathy with the simplistic useful/harmful judgements made on species, especially if they had never seen and appreciated the aesthetics of these rare denizens of the marshes. The Norfolk harriers also featured heavily in the work of famous bird artists of the day, notably Roland Green and J.C. Harrison.

The risk of disturbing the birds that photography undoubtedly brought was balanced against its important role. Earlier photographers all failed with the Marsh Harrier, but, with the guidance of Jim Vincent, the

Lancashire photographer Walter Higham took the first photograph of the species in Britain, of a female at a nest of young chicks in the early 1930s (reproduced in his 1949 book *Birds in Camera*). Buxton himself photographed the species, commenting 'in no instance have I secured a single photograph without six weeks' preliminary work, during which the hide has been gradually advanced from about three hundred yards towards the nest. Subterranean hides have been dug at dead of night by perching posts and feeding places, but never yet has the quarry failed to spot the new heap of rushes or the aperture for the lens'. In 1942, Eric Hosking took the famous series of photographs of Marsh Harrier at Hickling featured in his 1944 book *Birds of the Day*. He found two nests fathered by a polygynous cock (the first record of polygyny in Britain), but the birds were disturbed by local children playing nearby and deserted one nest. After that they would visit the other only quickly to deliver food. Eric and Dorothy Hosking fed the young themselves and one survived to fledge, probably the only one in Britain that year.

More recently, the difficulties encountered with photographing Marsh Harriers were described by Jack and Lindsay Cupper (1981). They found the Swamp Harrier the most difficult and wary of all the wide range of Australian raptors they worked with. Not only does it have having acute hearing, but it also apparently possesses a sense of smell, referred to by an earlier writer (Sharland 1947) who observed a youngster raise its head 'as a dog does when sniffing the air' and walk over to retrieve a piece of meat that had fallen out of sight. The Cuppers regarded this as the possible reason why the birds avoided a hide near the nest. They had to set up the hides no earlier than a week after hatching, downwind, well camouflaged and about 10 metres away at first. The hide was moved gradually closer. They remarked: 'This is one bird we suspect may be able to count a little so wherever possible we have a seeing-in party of more than one person – and a seeing-out party if we plan to return. So that the birds don't have to become re-accustomed to objects on the hide when the cameras and flash-heads are replaced we leave bottles and shiny tins in their stead'. The adults still stayed away for long periods, and siblicide resulted among the hungry young. The photographs do, however, lead to an important appreciation of the species, although mistakes should not be repeated.

For a long time, breeding Marsh Harriers were confined to Hickling and Horsea and were shot out of hand elsewhere. Up to five nests were successful on the two estates in this period, and for quite some time the species was Britain's rarest breeding bird. Very few nests were recorded elsewhere. True colonization of further counties was slow, but began in Suffolk in 1945 following the growth of large reedbeds as a result of the deliberate wartime flooding of coastal grazing marshes as an anti-invasion measure. Four young fledged from a nest near Lowestoft in 1945 and a second nest was suspected (Moore 1987). Coastal flooding in 1953 led to the abandonment of more grazing marsh to the water and reeds, at Kessingland, Minsmere and Walberswick. Two of these reedbeds survive now as famous reserves: Walberswick (English Nature) and Minsmere (RSPB). The species has bred at Minsmere every year since 1955. Less gamekeeping and the Protection of Birds Act 1954 assisted the birds' survival, and by 1958 there was a pre-crash peak of eight nests in Suffolk.

Nationally, a slow increase in the number of nests took place through the later 1940s and the 1950s. Breeding was recorded in seven counties. A pair nested successfully in Kent in 1942 (KOS 1981), in 1945 a pair fledged one young in Anglesey (Colling and Brown 1946), and a pair nested unsuccessfully in Hampshire in 1957 (Clark and Eyre 1993). The numbers dropped slightly in 1959, but much more severely in the next few years. Breeding was continu ous (up to five pairs) in Poole Harbour, Dorset, from the late 1940s to 1962 (Chapman 1977), but then ceased. Norfolk again lost the species in 1960, and there was much speculation about disturbance from the Broadland holiday boating industry and the effect of Coypu damage on reedbeds and sedge-beds. The severe winter of 1962/63 greatly reduced the number of Coypu, and the eradication campaign was soon under way. Although Marsh Harriers were seen each year in the Broads, they just would not breed. Instances of outlying nesting occurred in Lincolnshire (1962) and Yorkshire (1963–66) and possibly in Scotland (1966), but the first *Breeding Atlas* (fieldwork 1968–72) showed confirmed breeding at just four East Anglian sites during that period. By 1971 there was just one nest in the country, at Minsmere. The Marsh Harrier was Britain's rarest breeding bird of prey. The number of pairs breeding in Holland (Bijlsma 1993) and elsewhere showed a parallel decline, although they were already very depressed owing to persecution.

It was realized that the use of organochlorine pesticides (DDT, aldrin and dieldrin) was having a catastrophic effect on our populations of birds of prey. The proved effect on Marsh Harriers was a reduction in eggshell thickness, but the enigma is that in Britain, from the data available, this appeared to have no effect on those pairs that did breed in terms of number of young fledged from successful nests (Underhill-Day 1984). The thinning did, however, demonstrate susceptibility to these compounds, which were very probably harmful in other ways, and heavy metals and PCBs could have added significantly to the problem. In Sweden, Odsjo and Sondell (1977) proved that reduced success was correlated with the incidence of these substances in Marsh Harrier eggs, and no other credible cause has been found for the decline in harrier numbers in Britain at that time.

The second comeback: 1971 to the present day

Organochlorine pesticides were withdrawn in stages and the numbers of nesting Marsh Harriers in Britain began to rise, painfully slowly at first. A similar decline in other countries meant that numbers were low over a wide region of north-west Europe, and recruitment from nearby Continental countries was therefore slow. By 1976 British nests were again into double figures annually, and in 1980 attained the 20 mark. The increase was gain-ing pace, and the recolonization of Britain may well have been assisted by the spread of birds from the polders in the Netherlands. By 1990 the number of nests in Britain was in the range 82–115, and track was no longer kept of precise numbers (Rare Breeding Birds Panel). The great majority of these

ABOVE *Full adult male and typical adult female in food pass.*
BELOW *Sub-adult male and dark-headed female coming together for food pass.*

still centre on the Norfolk Broads, north Norfolk and Suffolk coasts, but there is increasing evidence of expansion of range, with more pairs breeding in Lincolnshire, Cambridgeshire and Kent, and nesting at sites in Avon and Somerset, Lancashire (Leighton Moss), Yorkshire (Humber), Wales (Anglesey) and Scotland augurs well for the future. Unexplained mysteries have been the failure to breed successfully in Essex, until one pair achieved this in 1992, and to recolonize Poole Harbour.

The age of blinkered gamekeeping largely disappeared with the social revolution of World War II. This helped the birds' prospects, which, together with the reinstatement and recognition of the value of reedbeds, allowed them to begin a comeback, but this was soon countered by the near disaster from pesticides. Legal protection for birds of prey in western Europe, for example in France from 1972, appears to have coincided with a recovery and therefore may have had a significant influence on shooting, despite widespread breaches of the law. Nevertheless, the principal hazard for migrating raptors remains to this day the pressure of shooting in southern Europe. Developments of significance elsewhere in western Europe have been the creation of massive reedbeds in Holland as part of the polder process of reclamation of land from the sea and the momentum gained by the nature-conservation movement as a whole, resulting in a significant proportion of the nesting population using nature reserves, where they are protected.

Research and researchers

British research on the Marsh Harrier began with watching from hides at Hickling and Horsey. Notes were published on behaviour and food by Buxton, Hosking, Vincent and others. In Suffolk, G.B.G. Benson published some useful notes in the late 1950s. The RSPB reserve at Minsmere, established in 1947, was developed by Herbert Axell from 1959 and, although the Marsh Harriers there were left alone, much information was gathered. Established more recently, Titchwell RSPB Reserve in north Norfolk holds 2–3 nests annually, and the harriers' food and hunting behaviour have been monitored, intensively in 1980–83, by Norman Sills and colleagues. John Underhill-Day has made intensive studies of the evolution of the British population, the diet of the species in the breeding season and its hunting. He has taken responsibility for keeping track of the data that have underpinned recent accounts of the decline and comeback of the species in Britain this century.

The harriers are among those birds which can evoke the most intense of passions in the enthusiast. Working from hides on the moors, in the plantations, or built of reed in the marshes of West Jutland, the Dane Henning Weis put so much effort into a pioneering study of Montagu's and Marsh Harriers that his colleagues could not help feeling that it had undermined his health when he died in 1922 at the early age of 30. His book *Life of the Harrier in Denmark* (1923) was published posthumously in Danish and English editions. Weis called the Marsh Harrier 'a creature of infinite caution and wariness towards everything unknown', but the fine period photographs which grace his book and show the whole of the breeding cycle testify to the success he achieved with the species.

In 1970, Jean-Marc Thiollay published an authoritative paper on the ecology of a population in the Camargue in the south of France. Intensive research in Holland and France in the 1960s and early 1970s by Wilhelm Schipper and his colleagues at the Free University of Amsterdam led to our first understandings of the mechanisms at play in the coexistence of sympatric harriers, especially with regard to their hunting and prey. A recent small complementary study by myself, André Bourgonje and Henk Castelijns on a saltmarsh in the south of Holland has thrown some light on the difficult area of winter diet. Work on Marsh Harriers in Holland has been continued by Menno Zijlstra, an expert on polders, Wibe Altenburg and colleagues on the specific case of Lauwersmeer polder, Dick Woets in the Weerribben, and Cor Dijkstra, who has studied survival and has wing-tagged many young in recent seasons. In 1973, Ebel Nieboer produced a remarkable dissertation on 'Geographical and Ecological Differentiation in the Genus *Circus*', extensively analysing the structural and plumage characteristics of harriers and putting forward hypotheses for their significance where several harrier species coexist. His research also came up with important theories on the evolution of harrier species and the history of their distribution, and was based on specimens drawn from museums all over the world. In response to a remarkable rise in Marsh Harrier numbers in Denmark since the early 1970s, Hans Jørgensen and the Danish Birds of Prey Group have published substantial papers on surveys and breeding biology. In Germany, Walter Bock studied the biology of a Marsh Harrier population in Schleswig-Holstein in the 1970s. As part of an ongoing research programme on Marsh Harriers under the auspices of the CRBPO of the French National Natural History Museum, Christian Bavoux and colleagues have published the results of studies of a wide range of aspects of both breeding and wintering birds in Charente-Maritime, western France, since 1983.

The most thorough account I have found published in English on the breeding biology of the species is undoubtedly that by Jøsef Witkowski at Wroclaw University, Poland. In almost 100 pages of the Polish journal *Acta Ornithologica*, Witkowski (1989) has written up his intensive research on a population of up to 50 breeding pairs of Marsh Harriers on six fish-pond complexes in the Barycz valley, western Poland, in the years 1972–75 and 1982–84. The comparison between the two periods is invaluable, since organochlorines and shooting were affecting the population in the first period, but not in the second. In Spain, Jøse González has extensively studied the species' status, breeding biology, diet and other aspects, published in the ICONA book *El Aguilucho Lagunero en España* in 1991. Farther afield, much academic research has been published on Swamp Harriers by Nick Fox in New Zealand and by David Baker-Gabb in both New Zealand and Australia. and on the African Marsh Harrier by Robert Simmons in South Africa. W.S. (Bill) Clark from the USA has made great strides with the understanding of harrier plumages. Indeed, research on harriers in general by these and others has reached such a peak that it was possible for the UK Hawk and Owl Trust to hold the first international symposium on the genus at the University of Kent in September 1993.

33

4

BREEDING DISTRIBUTION AND POPULATION TRENDS

Throughout much of their breeding range, members of the Marsh Harrier complex are part of a harrier population of mixed species co-existing in the same regions in 'sympatry'. In Britain, we are fortunate to have three species breeding out of the world's eleven or so species of harrier. Two of these, Marsh and Montagu's, breed side by side on the east coast. On mainland western Europe, lowland-breeding Marsh and Montagu's Harriers are joined by the Hen Harrier, which is also a lowland breeder there, in contrast to its upland range in Britain. In western Asia, Marsh, Montagu's and Pallid Harriers occur in the same regions in the south, and in north-west Kazakhstan, for example, I have seen all three breeding in the same marshes; the Hen Harrier is added farther north. In eastern Asia, Eastern Marsh, Pied and Hen Harriers coexist, and, in Australia, Swamp and Spotted Harriers.

World distribution

Confined to the Old World, the breeding distribution of members of the Marsh Harrier complex follows that of the other harriers in so far as it is restricted to the more temperate latitudes, both north and south of the Equator.

A lowland bird of open country, the Marsh Harrier's breeding range covers virtually the whole of Europe and stretches right across the Palearctic to about Lake Baikal, where it is replaced by the Eastern Marsh Harrier, which occurs between about the same latitudes. It covers temperate, Mediterranean, steppe, even desert zones down to a latitude of about 30°, and boreal zones up to one of about 65°. Within its range, the distribution is largely dictated by its wetland habitat, which can be either freshwater or brackish, but it avoids upland areas. The potential of the species has been greatly reduced generally by the drainage of wetlands for agricultural development, although neighbouring habitats are used some of the time for hunting, roosting and even nesting.

The race *harterti* is resident in north-west Africa, breeding in the coastal marshes of the Mediterranean and even at altitude by lakes in the Moyen Atlas at up to 1600–1800 m above sea level (Bergier 1987), but also in drier situations with dense vegetation (Giraud-Audine and Pineau 1974).

The Australasian Swamp Harriers are more similar in form to the nominate race than *spilonotus* and so presumably became isolated at a later time. The breeding distribution of the Swamp Harrier in Australia is confined to the north, east, south-east and south-west, avoiding the arid inland

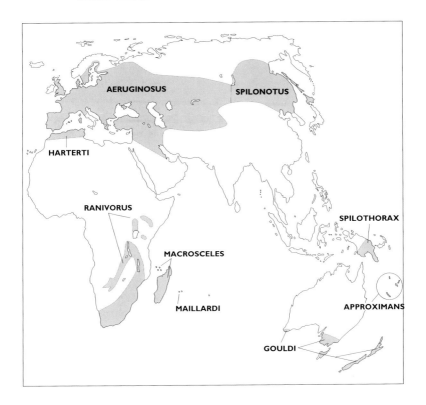

MAP 1 *Breeding ranges of Marsh Harriers.*

areas. A few Australian Swamp Harriers also visit Papua New Guinea in winter, but the resident Papuan Harrier is thought to descend from migrant Eastern Marsh Harriers coming from the north. Within New Zealand, Swamp Harriers are distributed throughout the country, having adapted more to dry habitats.

The best candidate for status as a species separate from the other Marsh Harriers forms, the non-migratory African Marsh Harrier probably evolved from a population isolated in southern Africa at an early stage. The extensive intervening band of forest around the Equator may have caused the isolation. The island forms of Marsh Harrier are also isolated and non-migratory – the Polynesian, Papuan, Réunion and Madagascar Harriers.

Britain

Being on the western edge of the range of the species, it is perhaps not suprising that Britain has been recolonized rather slowly. Coastal reedbeds have proved to be the prime habitat. Although odd pairs have now nested as far afield as Avon and Somerset, Lancashire, Yorkshire, Anglesey and

Fig. 1 *Number of Marsh Harrier nests in Britain 1971–1991*

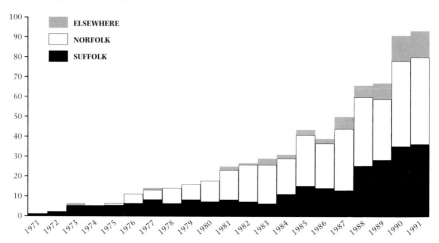

Scotland, the great majority breed in the coastal marshes of Norfolk and Suffolk. Neighbouring Lincolnshire has had a few nests annually at regular sites (eight pairs by 1992) since breeding began there in 1983. Surprisingly, Essex has lagged behind, the first successful nest there being as late as 1992. Beginning with solitary successful nests in 1983, 1984 and 1990 (Hadrill 1991), breeding on the Isle of Sheppey in Kent has recently assumed semi-colonial proportions, with five nests in 1991, eight in 1992, ten in 1993 and well into double figures in 1993 and 1994. Marshes beyond Kent on the south coast of England have not attracted breeding Marsh Harriers since the last nest in Poole Harbour in 1962.

Colonization of suitable reedbeds farther inland has been far slower. Isolated pairs have bred inland, but typically have not persisted at the same sites for more than a year or two. At Wicken Fen, the first nest was in 1981; subsequent breeding has been intermittent, in 1985, 1991, 1992 and 1994. At another Cambridgeshire site in the fens, a polygynous trio bred in 1987; a pair returned and bred there the following year, but none subsequently. Three other Cambridgeshire fenland sites have short or irregular histories of nesting. On the Somerset Levels, a successful nest in 1986 has been followed by a relatively long record of mixed failure and success, but so far as is reported not involving more than one nest each year.

A comparative study of the ecology of breeding harriers on the coast and inland remains to be carried out to pinpoint differences in food or other factors. The population at the main hotspot, on reclaimed farmland by the Wash, has expanded to utilize the smaller reedbeds and even crops as nesting sites, and the birds include much arable or grazing land in their hunting ranges. The constant breezes on the coastal strip may make it easier for the species to remain on the wing in search of prey. Also, coastal reclaimed land is generally rich in prey, which could be the most important factor. The population dynamics of the species also require careful study –

the loose colonial aspect of the harriers' breeding system may be important in sustaining the population of an area.

There are a number of popular bird reserves where Marsh Harriers breed regularly. In East Anglia, these include Minsmere and Walberswick in Suffolk, and Titchwell Marsh, Strumpshaw Fen and Hickling Broad in Norfolk. In the north, Leighton Moss in Lancashire is now a regular breeding site, with one or two pairs successful each year since the first nest in 1987. The tidal reedbed on the upper Humber River at Blacktoft Sands RSPB in South Humberside is one of the largest reedbeds in Britain outside East Anglia. Up to two pairs of Marsh Harriers bred there successfully from 1963 to 1966, but a nest in 1967 failed at the egg stage and successful breeding did not take place again until 1977 (Grieve 1977) and then not again until 1982. In 1994 two pairs bred there successfully and at least two other nests were known along the Humber. In the south, Elmley on the Isle of Sheppey in Kent now provides a good chance of seeing breeding birds.

The Marsh Harrier is principally a scarce spring and autumn passage visitor to Scotland, mostly in the east and north, with the bulk occurring in spring. Favoured localities are the reedbeds at Strathbeg on the north-east coast and Insh Marshes in the Spey Valley. The male of a pair seen nest-building at Dinnet Moss, Aberdeen, in 1980 was found poisoned shortly afterwards (Buckland *et al.* 1990). The exciting news that Marsh Harriers were again breeding in Scotland came in 1990, when two of four pairs were successful (Rare Breeding Birds Panel). A 'probable' breeding record in Anglesey in 1991 and a 'possible' record there in 1992 may mark the first return of the species to Wales as a breeding bird since a pair reared three young in 1973 and 'probably' bred in 1974 (Lovegrove *et al.* 1994). The situation in Ireland remains one of hope for future recolonization.

Europe

In overall terms, the population in western Europe has been firmly on the increase since the early 1970s.

Climatic changes and progressive eutrophication of lakes, encouraging the growth of reed and other vegetation, probably played a part in the growth of Marsh Harrier populations in Fennoscandia this century. The spread of the Marsh Harrier coincided with expansion of other species into the area – Black-headed Gull, Pochard, Coot, Great Crested Grebe and Lapwing (Hilden and Kalinainen 1966). The Marsh Harrier began to breed in Finland early in the century and the population has steadily increased to more than 200 pairs, expanding inland in recent years but disappearing for reasons unknown from many sites formerly occupied along the south coast (Saurola 1985).

In the early 1900s the Marsh Harrier was a very scarce breeding bird in Sweden. After an appreciable increase, surveys in 1958 and 1969 estimated populations of 150–175 and 200 pairs respectively. Observations were concentrated around the larger waters rich in reedbeds, with a few in the far south and around Öland. The distribution and size of the population did not seem to have changed significantly between the two surveys, but during the next decade an increase became apparent (Arvidsson 1980) and a survey in 1979 gave an estimate of 500 pairs (Bylin 1981). There was speculation as to whether greater observer awareness was the cause, but the increase was known to be real in the places where the population had been continuously monitored; the distribution had not changed. A decrease in numbers has been noted at some sites in the 1980s (Risberg 1990).

Denmark has seen a remarkable increase, with about 500 pairs breeding in 1983 compared with 100 in 1971 according to the Danish Birds of Prey Group survey (Jørgensen 1985) which cited legal protection in western Europe and reduced levels of DDT and other pesticides in the environment as the causes (ringing recoveries had shown that many Scandinavian birds were previously shot in France and Spain). The species is concentrated mainly in the south, this said to be because of lack of habitat and high rainfall in the north in June and July (Jørgensen et al. 1982).

In Germany, a steady decline until the early 1970s from the usual causes of shooting, habitat loss and pesticides was reversed, and estimates were 1500 birds (East) and 725–850 pairs (West) in the early 1980s (Génsbøl 1986). The recent atlas (Rheinwald 1993) gives a surprising figure of 10,000 for the united country.

Marsh Harriers are principally distributed throughout the low-lying areas of the Netherlands – the peat districts of Friesland and Noord-Holland, the Wadden Sea islands, the Delta area in the south-west and Zuidelijk Flevoland. The intense persecution and loss of habitat in the first half of this century and the effect of organochlorines were reversed by the advent of the new polders. The situation has seen a succession of developments. The largest polder, Zuidelijk Flevoland, was dammed in 1968 and was rapidly colonized throughout the 1970s. Numbers built up to about 400 nests, but rapidly fell through the 1980s to about 100 nests by 1990 as much marshland was reclaimed for its eventual purpose of agriculture. Overflow of birds from Flevoland may have assisted colonization of the marshes of the Delta area in the south-west, building up to about 270 pairs in 1991 (Meininger et al. 1992). A small population in Weerribben, just north-east of Flevoland, peaked at 20–25 nests in 1980, but has since severely decreased following wholesale cutting of reed (Woets 1986, in litt.). In the north, the Lauwersmeer polder was dammed in 1969 and numbers peaked at about 72 nests in the early 1980s. The Wadden Sea islands of Ameland, Terschelling and Texel have seen substantial increases in nests through the 1980s and by the early 1990s probably supported more than 100 nests. The latest national population estimate is 1370–1410 pairs (Bijlsma 1993).

In France, the 1979–82 FIR/UNAO survey estimate of 700–1000 pairs was thought to be somewhat pessimistic by Bavoux et al. in 1988. They noted a recent significant increase in the marshes of western France, which hold some of the highest densities of breeding harriers in Europe; increasing drainage of marshes for arable crops threatens these (Leroux 1991). Other areas of importance for the species in France are marshes of Lorraine and Champagne in the north, Vendée and the coastal reaches of the Loire in the west, Brenne in the centre and the Camargue in the south.

In Spain, accurate population figures are not available for the past but a considerable decline is apparent over recent decades, due largely to drainage and loss of habitat. The species is concentrated in four areas: the marshes of the Guadalquivir delta in the south, of La Mancha Humeda and the Tajo south-west of Madrid, of the upper reaches of the Ebro in the north-east, and the Duero in the north. There appears to have been some concentration of numbers owing to habitat loss in some of these areas. The species is absent in certain large wetlands, notably the Ebro Delta and Albufera in Levante, and Cornisa Cantabrica. A census in 1990 by the Grupo Iberico de Rapaces put the population at 481–522 pairs (Martinez *et al.* in Clarke in press).

A number of the populations in east European countries are very substantial, having benefited from the holding-back of commercial pressures on habitat. Recent figures are largely lacking, but estimates of up to 2000 pairs in Poland and up to 3000 pairs in Belorussia, where it is now one of the commonest raptors, are particularly notable. With the collapse of communism they now face intensification of land use and an uncertain future. In Russia, Galushin (1991) was quite positive about a comeback of Marsh Harriers where they had been absent for decades and an increase year by year during migration (e.g., along the west coast of the Caspian Sea).

Table 1. Latest breeding-population estimates for the Western Palearctic

Country	No. pairs	Country	No. pairs
Britain[1]	112	Albania	?
Ireland[2]	0	Greece[21]	130
Norway[3]	5th breeding record	Turkey[21]	100–250
Sweden[4]	400–500	Syria	0
Finland[6]	230	Iraq	?
Denmark[6]	500	Lebanon	?
Germany[6]	10,000	Jordan	?
Netherlands[8]	1370–1410	Israel	0
Belgium[4]	20–25	Egypt	0
France[9]	700–1000	Libya	0
Spain[10]	481–522	Tunisia[21]	50
Poland[11]	1500–2000	Algeria	?
Portugal[12]	40–50	Morocco[22]	100–500
Slovakia[13]	300–400	Russia (European)[22]	'Increasing'
Czech[13]	900–1100	Estonia[23]	100
Austria[14]	150	Latvia[23]	100
Switzerland[15]	0	Lithuania	?
Hungary[16]	1000	Belorussia[24]	2200–3000
Romania[17]	800	Ukraine (west)[25]	1200
Italy[18]	70–100	Georgia	?
Yugoslavia[19]	'Widely distributed'	Azerbaydzhan	?
Bulgaria[20]	50–70	Armenia	?

Sources [1]1992 – RBBP; [2]Hutchinson (1989); [3]1991 BB (1993); [4]Suetens (1989; [5]Rheinwald (1993); [6]Saurola (1985); [7]Jørgensen (1985); [8]Bijlsma (1993); [9]FIR/UNAO (1984); [10]Martinez *et al.* (in Clarke in press a); [11]Tomialojc (1990); [12]Ruffino (1989); [13]Danko *et al.* 1994; [14]Gamauf (1991); [15]*Der Ornithologische Beobachter*; [16]BB (1991); [17]Kalaber (1985); [18]Martelli and Parodi 1992; [19]Vasic *et al.* (1985); [20]Nankinov *et al.* (1991); [21]Génsbøl (1986); [22]Thévenot *et al.* (1985); [23]Galushin; [24]Ivanovsky (in Clarke in press a); [25]BB (1992);

Note: BB = *British Birds*, European News; RBBP = Rare Breeding Birds Panel. Number of pairs, although almost universally used, is not quite an accurate measure owing to varying degrees of polygyny in the populations.

5

HABITAT

The Marsh Harrier is essentially a bird of the wet first stages in ecological succession from water to woodland. Such habitat occurs of course at the water's edge on lakes, rivers and the coast, and is characterized by lush emergent vegetation. The habitats used by the species therefore do not generally include waterbodies such as reservoirs with cleared edges, but all types of freshwater marshes, fens, bogs, mires, saltmarshes, deltas, rivers, lakes, broads, lagoons and continental fish ponds where the water is still or slow-moving and the vegetation is allowed to grow. The harriers' activities spill out over the low-lying plains associated with these marshes, especially reclaimed land. The productivity of reclaimed and fen agricultural land shows how fertile such marginal habitat is.

In Britain, the largest wetland in historic times was the Great Level of the Fens, stretching inland from the east coast and the tidal waters of the Wash. Charles Kingsley (*Prose Idylls*, 1882) romanticized the soughing seas of reed and how 'high overhead hung, motionless, hawk beyond hawk, buzzard beyond buzzard, kite beyond kite, as far as the eye could see'. Even inland, countless floodplains and valley bottoms would have held smaller marshes with marvellous birds such as Common Crane, Bittern, Spoonbill and Marsh Harrier. The marshes, fens, meres, mosses, moors and bogs were not, however, pleasant places for people. They were dangerous for those who had to cross them and they brought malaria and other diseases. Close to centres of population, the pollution would make them even more of a hazard. They had to go. The contrast between the world of abundant marshes in which the Marsh Harrier evolved and today's tamed terrain is stark. The modern landscape is, perhaps more than we realize, the product of man's control over water and natural disasters such as flooding, which were once the prime force. Rivers are now canalized and confined within narrow banks where once they spilled out over wide floodplains and ended in complex deltas. In coastal areas, the inundations of the the sea have been controlled. Marshes are very much a habitat under threat.

Vegetation preferences

The Marsh Harrier is so closely associated with the Common Reed that its name in some of the major languages includes the word reed: Rohrweihe (German), Busard des Roseaux (French) and Rørhøg (Danish).

Nest sites are usually in dense, tall vegetation growing in water. The nests I have visited on foot in marshes have all required thigh waders and a certain amount of courage to reach. Reedswamp growth, principally Common Reed, is the vegetation mostly selected for nesting. Associated tall reedswamp plants include False Bulrush, Lesser Bulrush, Bulrush, Branched Bur-reed and Reed Sweetgrass. Fen vegetation is also used, such as Saw Sedge and rush, one stage on in the succession to woodland. I have also seen nests in flooded willow scrub, accessible only by boat. On saltmarshes, nests occur in reed and among other tall plants such as Sea Club-rush and Sea Aster.

Regional analyses of nesting habitats reveal the predominance of reed. In Britain up to 1982, all except two nests were in Common Reed or associated fen vegetation (Underhill-Day 1984); since then, about 10 per cent of nests have been in crops (Underhill-Day in Gibbons *et al.* 1993). In Flevoland, Schipper (1979) found only six out of 409 nests outside reedbeds. In Denmark, Jørgensen (1985) reported on 612 nests: 90 per cent in reedbeds, 7 per cent in other types of marsh and only 4 per cent in dry habitats. In western France, of 920 nests, Bavoux *et al.* (1989) found 55 per cent in reed, 12 per cent in bulrush, 7 per cent in Sea Club-rush, 5 per cent in tall grasses, 4 per cent in Saw Sedge and the remaining 17 per cent in a variety of other rank vegetation. Only 20 per cent of nests were in dry habitats, including 4 per cent in crops, and 71 per cent were in vegetation more than a metre deep. More of the early nests were in flooded reed, implying a preference for that by the older, more experienced and established birds; they had a higher success rate. In Schleswig-Holstein, Bock (1978) found 86 per cent of 147 nests in reeds, the rest in reedmace, sedge and crops.

Reed grows in fresh or brackish water up to about a metre deep, and on damp land. It does seed, but its principal method of spreading is by its root system or rhizomes, perhaps 1.5 m in a season. Freshly cut reeds grow in dense stands, typically up to 2 m tall, but in exceptional conditions up to 3 m or more. Marsh Harriers cannot nest after a winter cut, as they need old reed where they can hide their nest in early spring while the green reed of the year grows through. Old reed stems can remain standing for about three years. In winter, the brittle dead yellow reed is broken down in places by winter storms, snow and floods, providing the openings among standing reed which are used for roosting and later for nest sites. Heavy winter storms and floods can flatten large areas of reed and leave breeding harriers rather exposed in the following season (Arvidsson 1980). In some circumstances, harriers will flatten down patches to create platforms. Standing by a communal winter roost on the Dutch coast, I could clearly hear some of the harriers breaking down the reeds as they settled. Reedbeds provide good protection against many forms of predator and other disturbance. Bert Axell's comment on the human factor was evocative: 'whose progress through a reed bed is about as dainty as a bull in a china shop and, in summer, more harmful'.

As reedbeds mature and become drier, they are less attractive to Marsh Harriers. If the reeds are not harvested at all, the annual growth breaks down into a litter at the base of the bed and becomes a thick black ooze as it sinks into the water. Peat builds up from this, and reedbeds that are not managed turn into sedge fen or fen carr. This can happen surprisingly quickly, and so sustainable management of reed is important. Economic factors can play an important part in the survival of reedbeds. Reeds harvested less than annually are not so valuable for thatching since they contain old and decaying reed, but a mature reedbed is broken up by mats of the detritus of past seasons and provides the more diverse structure which Marsh Harriers prefer. A compromise is often required between conservation and commercial interests for the benefit of all (*see* Chapter 13).

A survey of England and Wales in 1979 and 1980 found 109 reedbeds of more than 2 ha (Bibby and Lunn 1981). Their distribution had a strong coastal bias and lay principally in Humberside, Norfolk, Suffolk, Kent, Hampshire and Dorset. Just 21 of the 109 were known to have been used by breeding Marsh Harriers. It used to be thought that extensive reedbeds were the essential requirement for Marsh Harriers to breed. Bibby and Lunn found an association between Marsh Harriers and sites of more than 20 ha but, even at that stage, breeding had begun to take place at a few sites of less than 5 ha. Many smaller reedbeds have now been colonized, and nesting has spread into arable crops in the catchment areas of reedbed sites. Isolated cases of breeding have also occurred on saltmarsh. In the last ten years, 40 per cent of nests in Britain have been in reedbeds of less than 25 ha and 10 per cent in crops (Underhill-Day in Gibbons *et al.* 1993)and these percentages are increasing. The use of crops is most prevalent in west Norfolk, where Marsh Harriers nest in winter wheat, barley and oilseed rape in the same areas where other pairs nest in small patches of reed in ditches. Eighty nests occurred in these crops during the twelve years from 1982 to 1993 (Image in Clarke in press a),a nest in barley in 1982 being the first record of use of an arable crop in Britain. Crop-nesting has now begun on the Isle of Sheppey in Kent, where oilseed rape has been used adjacent to nest sites in reed in fleets and ditches. No crop-nesting has been updated in Suffolk.

Witherby *et al.* (1940) first mentioned crop-nesting in a 'recently reclaimed cornfield' in central Spain where a few pairs are now breeding in cereal fields with other harriers, possibly as a result of loss of habitat elsewhere (Martinez *et al.* in Clarke in press a). In France, the campaign sta-

Arable farmland near the coast. Marsh Harriers will nest in both the reedy ditches and in the yellow-flowering oil-seed rape.

The nest is normally hidden in tall reeds.

tistics published by FIR for intervention to save nests in crops feature only a very small number of Marsh Harrier nests, as opposed to the large number of nests of Montagu's and some of Hen Harrier. Bakker (1949) found that Marsh Harriers breeding in reeds and club-rush in the Noordoost polder of the former Zuydersee during World War II were faced with rapid cultivation of the polder after the war and bred in the crops. However, it now seems that crop-nesting can also be the result of a local population expanding in an area favoured probably for its prey resources. Crop-nesting was commonly recorded early this century for the Swamp Harrier in Australia (Burrell 1910) and the usual problems were met, as 'summer harvesting uncovers many of its nests and the knife of the reaper frequently breaks eggs and beheads young birds' (Sharland 1947).

A number of records of tree-nesting at up to 15 m above ground are known for the Marsh Harrier in Europe and for the Swamp Harrier in New Zealand. The implication in all cases was that the harriers built the nests themselves. In at least one of these instances a traditional reedbed site had been flattened by winter floods, but in most cases suitable ground-nesting habitat seemed still to be available nearby.

In the rare instances when tree-nesting does occur, the nest is usually built on a bushy canopy.

Foraging

Marsh Harriers prefer a diversely structured environment, with variation in vegetation height and features such as ditches which offer them the most chances for surprise as they fly over these and suddenly appear at close quarters to prey hidden in them. They therefore tend to avoid large, uniform areas without tall vegetation. The hunting-niche separation of sympatric harriers has been extensively studied in Holland by Schipper *et al.* (1975) in winter and by Schipper (1977) in the breeding season. A clear difference was shown in the height of vegetation preferred for hunting both between species of harrier and between sexes of the individual species. Female Marsh Harriers preferred hunting over wet reedbeds, and males hunted there, too, but they exploited adjoining habitats with shorter vegetation more than the females did.

The habitats surrounding reedbed nest sites are all-important, with farmland species featuring heavily in the diet in some studies. In Flevoland, the dry reedbeds could provide few marshland bird prey, so a preference was shown for hunting in crops (Schipper 1977). Shifts in hunting-habitat preference from reedswamp to arable farmland can take place once there are young in the nest if the arable habitat provides a higher return. Mixed cropping gives even more options. In Norfolk, Sills (1984) found that the pea crop preferred as hunting habitat was far richer in insects than other crops and attracted the juvenile Starlings featuring heavily in the harriers' diet.

Roosting habitats

Marsh Harriers roost predominantly in reedbeds, but, in breeding areas where these are small, autumn communal roosts form in crops. Barley appears to be preferred, but other cereals are used, as are beans, potatoes, sugar beet and other crops. On the coast, alternative roosting habitat is on saltmarsh.

In winter, the presence of other species of harrier in good numbers often seems to draw Marsh Harriers into dry habitats such as grassland for roosting purposes, and even onto bare ground. I regularly saw several Marsh Harriers at a roost predominantly of Montagu's and Pallid Harriers in dry grassland in Gujarat, north-west India. The roost peaked at 2000 birds, the largest harrier roost recorded in the world in recent times (Clarke in press b).

Meinertzhagen (1956) reported a group of 66 migrant male Marsh Harriers roosting together for one night on ploughed land in Afghanistan. In eastern India, Donald (1905) witnessed a roost of 'crowds' of Marsh, Pallid and Pied Harriers on bare ground. He concluded that they were not passing migrants, as they scattered in all directions in the morning.

On 22 January 1993, I was taken to a communal harrier roost in the Little Rann of Kutch, a desert in Gujarat, north-west India. The roost site was 1–2 km inside the desert, where the ground is flooded by the sea in the monsoon, but dries out from about September into a flat surface of cakes of salty mud. Arriving at the roost six minutes after sunset, we counted 11 harriers already standing on the desert; 20 minutes after sunset there were at least 20, but our position was rather too distant from the main concentration to make a satisfactory final count. The following evening we positioned ourselves more centrally and our final count was 30 harriers: about 20 roosted in one main group spread over about 500 m of desert, with several outliers, mostly in a small, loose sub-roost a further 500 m away. Those close enough to be identified by telescope were as follows: Montagu's Harriers – 3 adult females, 7 adult males; Pallid Harrier – 3 juveniles, 1 adult male; Marsh Harrier – 7 adult females or juveniles. This roost was not just a temporary phenomenon, since our guide, Anil Mulchandani, had found similar roosts in the area both the previous winter and earlier that same winter. In the absence of vegetation in which to hide, the harriers clearly must rely on their hearing to protect themselves at night. The dried mud had in many places formed a crust of small 'tiles' with raised edges and separated by cracks;a human foot spanned two or three and produced a crackling sound as weight was put onto it. Mammalian predators must also find it difficult to walk silently on this

crust, and this prompts the thought that harriers may choose their traditional roost sites on the criteria of where they can hear best from. We saw
Desert Fox, Indian Fox, Jackal and Wolf on the desert.

Habitat formation

In Britain, the widespread draining and destruction of marshes had largely
been completed by the turn of the century and there have been few losses
since, and a few gains. In Suffolk, flooding was employed as a coastal-de-
fence measure during World War II on low land at Minsmere, Walberswick
and Kessingland. The sluices to the sea were closed and fields were flooded.
Reed spread across from the network of dykes. Kessingland was subsequently drained, but Minsmere and Walberswick remain as large reedbeds.

In the Netherlands, land reclamation has allowed the study of the evolution
of the population of harriers from the beginning of the habitat succession
process. First, a polder is created by containing an area of shallow water in
banks. It is then pumped dry and sown with reed to begin the succession to
dry land. The important new polders of recent times are the Lauwersmeer in
the north and Oostelijk (east) and Zuidelijk (south) Flevoland in the west of the
country. Flevoland was the largest recent land-reclamation project in the
Netherlands and in Europe. The first stage, Oostelijk Flevoland, was begun in
the late 1950s, at a time when harriers were more persecuted (and soon to be
affected by pesticides, too). The second stage, Zuidelijk Flevoland, was embanked and pumped dry in 1968 and most of the 43,000 ha were sown with
reed. As parts were reclaimed for agricultural use, the area of reed fell from
about 41,000 ha in the early 1970s to about 4000 ha in 1980. Despite this,

*An immature Marsh Harrier – one of 30 harriers the author saw roosting
together that night on bare desert in India. This is unusual – harriers normally
roost amongst rank ground vegetation.*

A male leaving a reedbed nest site to hunt. Reedbeds are their principal habitat, but to obtain sufficient prey for the young the male often hunts over farmland.

the Dutch Marsh Harrier increased dramatically throughout the 1970s and there were about 400 nests in Flevoland at its peak in the late 1980s.

The Lauwersmeer was embanked in 1969. The first Marsh Harriers bred there in 1972, and by 1982 there were 72 pairs (Altenburg *et al.* 1987) nesting in seed and willowherb on 6700 ha of earlier land reclamations, salt-marshes and sand flats with 2400 ha of water in channels and gullies.

Habitat-niche expansion

In north-west Africa, Giraud-Audine and Pineau (1974) recorded how the race *harterti* was still breeding in areas where marshland habitat had been lost, using dry sites in bramble scrub, woods or plantations chosen for the density of their vegetation. The harriers were hunting in dry habitats, too, showing further adaptation to these.

Fox (1977a) remarked on the New Zealand Swamp Harrier's occupation of dry habitats. The harrier is one of the few native New Zealand birds to benefit from European settlement – the conversion of forest into open pasture and the introduction of small mammals and rabbits. Most New Zealand harrier nests found by Baker-Gabb (1981) were in dune hollows with long grass and rushes, and distant from water. The implication is that this is related to the niche expansion of the harrier there in the absence of competition from other diurnal raptors apart from the dissimilar New Zealand Falcon.

Other examples exist of the possible directions for habitat shift. For example, the Réunion Harrier has adapted to hunt in a forest environment (*see* Chapter 10).

6

BREEDING BIOLOGY

Age of first breeding

Some immature Marsh Harriers remain on the wintering-grounds in Africa or India in summer. Others colonize unoccupied or newly developed breeding habitats and some fill vacancies in the adult breeding population. In many raptor species, females are recruited into the breeding population earlier in life than males. Reliable information on the ages of breeding female Marsh Harriers is difficult to obtain by observation alone, since their plumage can be difficult to age. With males the position is clearer: full adult plumage is reached in their third or fourth calendar-year, and the age of younger birds can be gauged by their plumage (*see* Chapter 2). Although many sub-adult males are predominantly brown above, their light under-wings are soon obvious, and it is uncommon to find a male Marsh Harrier beginning to breed in true juvenile plumage with mainly brown under-wings. However, this does occasionally happen, probably mostly at new sites where there is no competition from established males. For example, the male of the first pair to breed in Cambridgeshire in the twentieth century was in brown plumage and gradually moulted into dingy male plumage during breeding. Several young males have been noted breeding in the initial stages of the new semi-colony on the Isle of Sheppey in Kent (P. Hadrill, pers. comm.). As a general rule, older males return earlier to the breeding-grounds, begin the breeding cycle earlier in the year than immature birds, and have greater success (Altenburg *et al.* 1987).

The age structure of the Marsh Harrier summering population seems to vary between the north and the south of Europe. In the Camargue, Thiollay (1970) recorded that, of a sample of 330 observations in spring, only about 28.5 per cent were of adult birds. He estimated that about 30 immatures were present in the area containing up to seven or eight breeding pairs, a predominance which may be more typical of marshes in southern Europe. Altenburg *et al.* (1987), who studied the evolution of a population which began to colonize Lauwersmeer polder in the Netherlands in 1969, found that when habitat first became suitable for breeding younger males predominated, but not in later years. They assessed that up to 20 non-breeding Marsh Harriers in immature plumage were present throughout the breeding season with up to 72 pairs which were breeding, indicating that about 12 per cent of birds present were non-breeding immatures. In Poland, Witkowski (1989) noted only 1–3 unmated territorial males in subadult plumage and up to five unpaired juvenile females among 30–50 breeding pairs. Observations in one well-recorded area in east England in 1988 suggested that about 34 per cent of the summering population were non-breeders there (Rare Breeding Birds Panel). For Britain, over the period 1947–80, Underhill-Day (1984) found a highly significant correlation between non-breeding summering birds and the number of breeding attempts in the following year. This may be expected in a recovering population.

Timing of the breeding cycle

The Marsh Harrier begins to nest earlier in the year than other harriers. This follows the general rule among raptors that larger species begin their longer breeding cycles earlier.

They return to breeding areas north of the wintering range from mid March to early May, depending on latitude (Glutz von Blotzheim *et al.* 1971). On the east coast of England individuals take up territory from March. The passage of migrants brings new birds into sites until mid May and stimulates territorial behaviour. In western Poland, Witkowski found that the return of males peaked at the end of March, but that of females in mid April. Bengtson (1967) in Sweden found that males usually return ten days before females. Spring migration statistics from the Mediterranean show that males migrate significantly earlier on average.

Courtship commences immediately the birds return, and the nest is normally built in about 2–3 weeks. Incubation begins with the first egg and lasts about 33 days. The young hatch asynchronously and stay in the nest for about 28 days. They are brooded continuously by the female for the first few days but gradually become more mobile and venture into the surrounding vegetation, returning to the nest to be fed. From about 28 days, the young can fly, but mostly sit about in the vicinity, typically on bushes; from about 45 days they fly around more but are still fed; from about 73 days they are more independent.

A clear relationship can be shown between latitude and the mean date of commencement of the clutch. In Spain and the south of France, many pairs begin laying in early or mid April. In England, the Netherlands and Poland, all at about the same latitude, the second half of April is the normal time, and farther north, in Scandinavia, clutches are begun in the second week of May. There also appears to be a differential between coastal and inland sites. I have suspected this from casual observation at the few inland nests in England, and Hildén and Kalinainen (1966) measured this in Finland, where the mean first laying date was 9 May on the coast, but 14 May inland. Schipper (1979), Witkowski (1989) and González (1991) all established that laying date was influenced by temperature. Laying began a few days after a rise in temperature, but only at the right time of year and if there was not a subseqent sharp cold spell. The rule put forward by Schipper (1979) for the Netherlands was as follows: 'The first date after 9 April with a temperature of over 4 °C followed by at least two days of temperature rise, whereas on the third or fourth day the temperature should not fall more than 28 per cent.' Apart from the obvious benefits of laying eggs in warmer, more settled temperatures, the key to this rule probably lies in the sychronization of breeding with the peak availability of young of waterfowl and other prey.

Copulation

Copulation is difficult to observe, generally taking place on the ground in a reedbed, on a cock's nest or convenient low perch. The female crouches down while the male stands on her back for several seconds, with sideways movement of the tail, wings outstretched and slowly beating to maintain balance. Next to no information is available on copulation rates etc. for the Marsh Harrier, but the most comprehensive study of copulation by harriers is that of Simmons (1990) on the African Marsh Harrier. Typically, copulation occurred early in the morning and was instigated by incessant uttering of a far-carrying whistle by the female as the male approached. Simmons used raised vantage points so that he could see down into the reedbed, and he found that copulation took place 50–220 times up to the completion of the clutch. The higher rates occurred where nests were close to others, showing the effects of competition. Copulation continued after laying, but dropped to about once a day.

Recent advances in DNA analysis have led to the discovery of some interesting facts on cuckoldry among birds in general. Extra-pair copulation has been shown to be more frequent than might have been assumed. A high rate of copulation increases the male's chances of paternity. Copulation rates are generally high among raptors, but, since the males have to spend long periods of time away foraging extra-pair copulation would appear to be quite likely. In fact it appears to be low among raptors. Simmons observed extra-pair copulation in only 2 per cent of 196 attempted copulations, and then it was solicited by the female.

Nest-site tenacity

Marsh Harrier breeding sites are generally traditional. The nest is not normally placed in the exact same spot, but in the immediate area. Breeding-site fidelity has not often been established with absolute certainty, but from the annual recurrence of birds at the same sites it seems to be the rule. Weiss (1923) noted that 'an old couple will often exhibit quite an astonishing degree of faithfulness to one particular patch of reeds'. In central Sweden, Sondell (1970) noted that three pairs identified by plumage characteristics all returned the following year and bred in the same parts of the reedbeds. In Lauwersmeer, Altenburg et al. (1987) found nests in the same places each year, even in vast reedbeds. Witkowski (1989) recorded one distinctive male holding the same nesting territory for four years and another for two.

The rate of return to the natal area for nesting may be low. Witkowski noted very few ringed birds recruited into the breeding population in his study, but confirmatory data from other studies are lacking. Of 32 adult birds ringed in eastern Europe and recovered from May to July, 16 were less than 50 km from their ringing site and five others were within 200 km. The most extreme of the rest were birds aged four and ten years recovered in north-west Africa in late May and mid July, respectively. Individuals recovered in the spring and summer of their second calendar-year showed a greater degree of return to their natal area: 13 out of 22 were within 50 km and all but two of the rest were within 200 km of their ringing site (Ilyichew 1982).

Nest-building

The nest is built quite rapidly over a few days, sometimes with both sexes taking part. Thiollay (1970) found that males were most active in bringing material, whilst females busied themselves at the site. Females seem to decide on the position of the nest. For some males, nest-building seems to be more a territorial ritual than a practical exercise. Some researchers have found that males do not participate. Weis said that he never saw a male bring material for the female's nest, only for a cock's nest, and 'when he does now and then come winging along with a reed as long as a small fishing rod, or, as a particularly

Newly-fledged young will harass the incoming male for food.

valuable prize, a wisp of straw from somebody's wooden shoe, there is often a touch of something like humorous enjoyment in his manner, as if he found it quite amusing'. However, I have seen both male and female building the same nest at a furious rate. The birds carry material in either their feet or their bills. They often use quite substantial pieces, a metre or more long, and the sight of a harrier riding a long reed stem like a witch's broomstick carried in both feet is quite entertaining. Materials used in the construction of the nest are taken from the nest territory, mainly reed, False Bulrush, bulrush, sedge, grass, willowherb, orache, dock, roots, twigs (willow, birch etc.) and in fact sizeable plant stems of any type. The lining is of finer material such as grass, rush or flowering reed-heads, brought by the female.

The nest is initially quite small, often supported above the water on a tangle of old reeds. The birds probably bend over and crack reed stems to provide the initial platform. Its overall diameter is in the range 42–100 cm, with a cup 10–35 cm in diameter and 6–8 cm deep (Glutz von Blotzheim et al. 1971). The nest steadily grows in size and can become a very substantial pile of material. Maintenance of the nest by the adding of material is important in order to keep the contents above water in the unstable marsh environment when it is constantly trampled by the young, particularly in wet weather, and also helps to keep the nest clean. This aspect has been studied in Spain by Fernandez (1992). Material was added steadily throughout incubation and this increased after hatching to reach a peak between days 12 and 22 of the nestling period, and then dropped off. More than 85 per cent of the material was supplied by the female. The role of the male was important during the first days of the nestling phase when the female was concentrating on brooding, but decreased as he had to hunt for more of the time. Most material was brought early in the day, possibly to compensate for the accumulation of damp in the nest during the night, and in the first part of the nestling period the supply increased significantly on rainy days, especially after storms. Nests built in dry habitats can be much less substantial: Witherby (1928) was shown one with four eggs in a barley field in central Spain which was 'very slight, having a foundation of a few thistle-stalks with barley as a lining'.

The male usually constructs one or more separate 'cock's nests' or platforms. These lack a finer lining. Observation of such construction activities early in the season by as yet unmated males can lead to erroneous assumptions of nesting. Cock's nests are used as roosting sites by the male and can be used as the focus of his skydancing, where he lands after his giddy descent. He may often take food there, and the female may go there to receive it instead of in the air.

Egg-laying and clutch size

Just prior to egg-laying the female stays close to the nest, food being brought to her by the male. His deliveries of prey increase as her time approaches and she takes less and less part in display, nest-building and territorial defence.

The eggs are generally laid at intervals of 2–3 days, although González (1991) established a shorter mean interval of 1.6 days in four clutches. Four or five eggs are the norm, and mean clutch size throughout Europe averages 4.5 eggs (range of means from separate studies/regions 3.7 to 5.2). Clutches of three or six eggs are unusual, and seven is really exceptional. Buxton recorded clutches of seven, seven and eight laid in successive years (1934–36) by one hen at Horsey. A clutch of eight eggs was photographed by Eric Hosking in the Hickling-Horsey area in 1943.

Clutches started earlier in the year tend to be larger (Altenburg *et al.* 1982; Bavoux *et al.* 1989; Witkowski 1989; González 1991), as found in many raptors. In western France, the modal clutch size was four, but five was almost as common (Bavoux *et al.*). However, it was found that success in terms of both hatching rate and fledging rate was highest for five-egg clutches; four and six-egg clutches also performed well, but those of two and three egg clutches had much less success. Witkowski found that four and five-egg clutches were the most productive in successful nests. Underhill-Day (1984) found a similar relationship between clutch size and fledging success in Britain, with 4-egg clutches producing the most fledged young in successful nests. The experience of Weis (1923) in one area of Denmark was that four eggs were the norm and four young were raised, but in another area where larger clutches were laid only three young fledged. His comments suggested that the latter showed selection for the strongest, producing more powerful offspring which in turn laid larger clutches – perhaps a fanciful theory.

Hatching success is related to laying date, with less success for later clutches (González 1991). Bengtson (1967) commented on the poor hatching success of the species. Vincent (undated) remarked on the effect of interference on the success of the early nests in Broadland, and Underhill-Day (1984) later found a significantly higher failure rate of nests in Britain during 1911–44 compared with the subsequent period. Nests were visited much more readily before legislation protecting them from disturbance came in from 1954.

The eggs of all harriers are white. In this respect, the harriers strangely follow hole-nesters that conceal their eggs. Rarely, some markings of red/brown have been claimed for the eggs of some species of harrier, including the Marsh Harrier. Marsh Harrier eggs have a bluish or greenish tint when fresh, but quickly turn a chalky white. Marsh Harriers will re-lay if the first clutch is lost, provided the season is not too far advanced. Witkowski (1989) recorded 17 replacement clutches, nearly all in May.

Incubation and hatching

The female begins incubation early during laying, generally with the first egg, but sitting is often not continuous until the second or third egg. The clutch begins to hatch after about 33 days (Witkowski 1989, Gonzalez 1991), generally asynchronously, although the first two or three eggs sometimes hatch together. The female relies on the male for food during incubation, but the rate of deliveries drops towards the end of laying as she needs less.

Few people can have studied behaviour at the nest during incubation; the species is notorious for its readiness to desert at this stage, but Weis (1923) managed get hides up at nests with complete clutches and describes how the sitting female will alternately doze and be fully alert, watching any bird passing. She pays attention to any sound, causing her to turn her head frequently, but strangely stretching up on her long legs to try and see what is approaching before she takes to the air. Weis described how she will lay down any material she has brought and turn the eggs when returning to the nest after a feed. Witkowski (1989) erected hides at two nests during incubation; he observed that when it rained the females often stood up to shake the water off, and in heavy rain they stood over the eggs, bent at an angle of 50°, the water running down their backs and tails away from the eggs. Bengtson (1967) found, from observations at five nests, that the male incubated for 10 per cent of the time; he also quoted wider experience of it ranging from none to 20 per cent, but this may be triggered by the female's temporary absence for one reason or another, rather than being any true sharing of the duty.

Feeding behaviour

The young take morsels of food from the female's bill from about eight hours after hatching (Witkowski 1989). At first they are given only the meat, but soon begin to take fur and feathers roughage with it, and the first, small pellets are cast from about seven days (Sach 1967). At about 23–25 days they begin to grab whole prey and pull it apart for themselves. The stronger young are more successful in claiming food from the female. The smaller ones have to wait until their larger siblings are satiated and they can take over the remains or claim the next prey to be brought in.

The rôles of male and female in feeding the young are usually quite clear-cut. On sensing the presence of the male, a hungry female will 'cheep' to him from the nest (Witkowski 1989). If the coast is clear, a male approaching the nest with prey will call her off. His manner of passing the food to her – the aerial food-pass – is an especially beautiful piece of harrier behaviour with several variants (see Chapter 7). Alternatively, he may take the food to a platform in the reeds some distance from the nest and the female will fly over to take the food on the ground. If the coast is not clear, he flies by the nes. Witkowski noticed a 'tilt' in flight to warn the female and she remained silent on the nest. The male provides all food for about the first ten days, passing it to the female generally away from the nest and visiting the nest himself only if she is not there, although some males do deliver prey direct to the nest. The males' delivery rate increases as the young grow and before the female begins to hunt. It probably depends on brood size, but studies have established means of about 11 (Underhill-Day 1989) or 12 (Witkowski 1989) items per day; performance ranged from 3 items to 20 in Witkowski's study. All feeding of the young is normally done by the female, but there are records of the male taking over this function if the female is lost. Witkowski recorded this at one nest where the male alone successfully reared young from 11–17 days, and Fernández and Azkona (1992) later in the breeding cycle (37–38 days) at a nest in Spain when a widowed male increased his prey deliveries and attendance at the nest. The female does not normally go far from the nest in search of food until the young are about ten days to two weeks old. She is able to catch larger prey than the male and provide the boost to the food supply necessary at the most demanding stage in the development of the young. She may deliver as many items as the male does (Witkowski).

The female is often described as turning completely upside-down to take the food pass from the male. This is in fact rare and may be restricted to instances where the male is reluctant to release his prey.

Growth and development

Newly hatched young are thinly covered in a white down, their pink skin showing through. They have large dark eyes, pink legs and feet, light-coloured claws, a blackish upper mandible with a tiny white knob towards the tip (the egg tooth) and lighter lower mandible. The cere is pinkish-yellow and soon turns fully yellow. Their shape is somewhat ugly; they have a large

The female normally takes the food pass by reaching out sideways in a roll or forwards as she rears up in the air.

head with a scrawny neck and a bulging round crop (if they are being adequately fed) distinctly separate from the abdomen, and a pointed rear. When they first become mobile they start to rest on their tarsi. The first down is replaced from about day five by a thicker buff-white down on the scapulars, wing and abdomen sides. The legs and feet turn yellow and the claws black, and the young generally become a lot more appealing. The facial disc becomes clearly differentiated, carrying less down and dark greenish in appearance around the eye and forward to the cere. The ear openings are clearly apparent to the rear of the corner of the gape. The tongue is reddish-pink. They put on weight slowly at first, but the rate increases sharply from about day five to eight and is steady and rapid until it begins to slow down and level off at about day 20 peaking at around 525 g for males and 725 g for females at 30–35 days (Witkowski 1989; Gonzalez 1991). The first feathers to begin emerging, initially in sheaths, are the scapulars, primaries and secondaries. These are visible from about one week and grow steadily from then. The young are fully feathered by day 35, except for patches of down lingering on the forehead and elsewhere. Witkowski gives the times of first flight as 37–39 days for males and 41–44 days for females. A significant drop in the supply or quality of food over a period will delay development and prolong the nestling period.

Behaviour at the nest

The young are generally brooded constantly for up to ten days, before they get their second down and begin to break into feather. It is important for the female to shield them from the heat of the sun and from chilling rain; Schipper (1979) noted frequent mortality after periods of rain.

Nest sanitation is generally maintained by the female until the later stages. She removes debris such as uneaten food remains, bones, pellets and eggshells. The young themselves, once mobile, crawl to the edge of the nest, lift their rear and shoot their faeces over the edge. If the nest is visited, young ten days old or more move away from the observer and those more than about 20 days old more readily put on a threatening display, opening their bills wider in a hiss as they are more closely approached, and they can react to attempts to touch them by getting on their backs to strike up with their talons. At older ages they will half extend their wings in the display.

The young are alert to the movement of an adult, lifting themselves up and cheeping weakly in anticipation of food. From about 12 days they are interested in everything, turning their heads and watching the reeds move and insects flying about. When they can walk, at some nests they begin to make tunnels where possible into the surrounding vegetation, into which they disappear if the adults give a warning call. The young will also take food into tunnels, protecting it from the others by mantling it. The use of such retreats, which can be 10-15 m long, may also help to keep the nest clean and afford the young some shade. In the later stages, an adult arriving at the nest with food may have to call and wait for a young harrier to appear to fetch the prey. At other sites, thick reeds and water may prevent them wandering. The young will try to catch things in their feet, perhaps an insect, and steal food from their siblings. They preen, picking down off their plumage, and exercise. Increasingly they will jump and perform wing-flapping exercises on the nest, and leave the nest to drink or bathe in hot weather. They bathe by ducking down in the water and rising, flapping their wings and moving their hindquarters up and down. As they get older the young climb about in the reeds, walking up reed stems eventually flapping their wings to learn to fly.

Siblicide is a well-known feature of raptor broods. Made possible by the size differences between young caused by asynchronous hatching of the eggs, in many eagles that lay just two eggs it appears to be the rule. In medium-sized raptors with larger broods it is generally interpreted as an adaptation to cope with an unpredictable food supply, enabling the brood size to adjust to the food supply. Weaklings that do not put on weight are quickly attacked, and may be eaten by their stronger siblings if torn up for them by an adult. Siblicide between healthy chicks is the product of hunger and occurs when the male fails to find enough prey. Jim Vincent was of the opinion that in Broadland Marsh Harriers siblicide was caused by hunger due to prolonged interference by photographers keeping the adults away. Vincent's point was underlined by Buxton, who quoted an instance of the adults being kept away from a brood of five by two men weed-cutting, 'lunch was late and in their impatience the three biggest chicks killed and ate the two smaller ones'. Cupper and Cupper (1981) found that siblicide was the result in the

Asynchronous hatching results in a wide range of ages in a brood. This can lead to siblicide if food is short.

Swamp Harrier in Australia when the adults were kept away by fear of their photographers' hide. Witkowski (1989) also observed siblicide and explained how aggression was triggered in the stronger young by not being offered prey, and by weakly and abnormal behaviour by the victim, including a twittering 'erick-erick' call. The potential for conflict lessens as their growth levels off and the competition for food is not so intense.

Fledging rates

Fledging rates per nest have been published from a large number of European studies. The mean number fledged from all nests started ranged from 1.6 to 3.3, and the fledging rate from successful nests, or the mean size of fledged broods, ranged from 1.9 to 3.4. Typically, these values are in the region of 2.6 and 3.3 respectively. Underhill-Day (1984) calculated the performance of British broods at 2.2 per nest started and 2.9 per successful nest, slightly below par. Together with a high desertion rate in the early years, this may have played a role in the slow recovery of the British population. The results of a number of past studies may have been affected by organochlorines, but one of the more recent and extensive studies, by Bavoux et al. (1989) in western France, found two or three young fledged as the norm (mean 2.5) at successful nests. Averaged over all nests started, this fell to a surprisingly low 1.6. They commented that the more sedentary population in France may have different demographic characteristics compared with the wholly migratory populations in northern Europe, including a higher survival rate and recruitment into the breeding population earlier in life.

Post-fledging

Newly fledged young sit around quietly, in the reedbed or typically on bushes or other raised perches. Prey is at first still taken to the nest for them, but they soon fly up to meet and harass the incoming adult for food with a whinnying, importuning whistling. The adults encourage them to catch food in the air. About two weeks after they fledge, the young begin to hunt for themselves.

González (1991) found that young he marked with wing tags moved only short distances up to two months of age, but were sighted at significantly longer distances after then. Dispersal was mainly south or south-west.

A fledgling Marsh Harrier.

Harriers building a nest will bring material in their bill or talons. When they use their talons they transfer the material to their bill immediately before they land.

Sex ratios

Sexing of young in the nest is best done as close to fledging as possible and can be based on three criteria: body weight, tarsus length and colour of irides. It is best to use a combination, because of individual variation. As a rule, male body weight at fledging is under 600 g, their tarsi do not exceed 84 mm and their irides are light brown. Females exceed 680 g, and have tarsi over 88 mm and dark brown irides (Witkowski 1989). Sex ratios in broods have not been shown to be slightly in favour of males (Witkowski 1989; Krijgsveld and Dijkstra in Clarke in press a). It has been calculated that parental investment in male and female young is similar in the wild (Witkowski 1989), but laboratory study has found a greater input required per female young (Krijgsveld and Dijkstra). Males are smaller, but they grow faster, are more active and fledge on average five days earlier. The larger females are less active and grow more slowly.

The occurrence of polygyny suggests an imbalance towards females among mature adults, although slower maturation of males may also have an effect on the sex ratio in the breeding population.

Nest watches

Nest watches on a normal field trip will be carried out from a safe distance without the benefit of a hide. What can the average observer expect to see? Delving into my notebook, a typical such watch on 5 July 1987 went as follows. The site was just outside a Cathedral city, with the great church as a backdrop, along with a busy river and railway! A polygynous male was mated with two females with nests 0.5 km apart. He was paying little attention to one. Of particular interest at this site was the intensive use of a willow tree.

7.12 a.m. Female flew in from the north-east carrying a small item of prey and alighted on the bare branch halfway down the harriers' favourite riverside willow; male suddenly flew out of the tree and down to the near-by nest.

7.17 a.m. Up he rose, out of the reeds, turning in the early-morning sun for a couple of minutes and settling in the top of the willow.

7.27 a.m. Female flew down from the willow to the nest.

7.30 a.m. Male left the tree; weathering the onslaught of Lapwings and Redshank, he skimmed across the riverside meadow and over the floodbank to hunt out on the arable.

8.13 a.m. He arrived back carrying prey and alighted on the branch; the nearest female flew up to take the prey from him on the branch, he immediately descending into the reedbed.

8.19 a.m. She flew off the branch with the prey in her bill, down into the reedbed.

8.20 a.m. Male flew up and over to another place in the reeds, flapping about and down; soon he was up and flapping/gliding away through the trees, and I had a glimpse of him farther downstream a minute or two later.

8.39 a.m. He arrives back, carrying, nest material prey circles low over the reeds but is not met, and he flies over to land on the willow branch.

8.49 a.m. Where is he? I noticed him shake himself, but not leave!

8.52 a.m. There he is, low over the reeds with nest material in his feet. He goes down. And again, the delivery of material is repeated.

8.53 a.m. He flies away over the floodbank.

9.21 a.m. Female in the air, landing down in the reeds away from the nest. She is soon up, nest material in her bill, and goes back to the nest.

10.35 a.m. After nine trips with nest material over the last hour and a quarter, she flies to their branch.

10.47 a.m. Suddenly I'm aware that the male is back, and almost at once there's a mid-air food-pass; she planes down into the reeds, and he retires to the branch.

Such watches begin to build up a picture of prey-delivery rates and behaviour, participation of the female in hunting, nest repair etc., surprisingly quickly.

7

SOCIAL BEHAVIOUR AND DISPLAYS

Voice

In the changeable climate of late March, I was battling into the wind along a Suffolk coastal path through the pale yellow of a winter reedbed. Suddenly I became aware of an insistent call. I had to search the heavens very carefully to pinpoint the source of this wild cry – a male Marsh Harrier putting himself through his undulating spring display far above the marsh. He had certainly attracted my attention and attention-attracting was clearly the purpose of his performance. It was too early for carrying nesting material, too early for food-passes, but with his 'song' he was making it very plain that he was on station.

Apart from breeding-season calls associated with courtship display, the passing of food and alarm, harriers appear to be very silent birds.

The courtship call of the Marsh Harrier is of an entirely different type from the chattering call of the displaying Hen, Montagu's and other harriers. It is a far-carrying cry and I find it difficult to describe. It is medium-pitched, lasts for rather less than a second, and certainly tails off a touch towards the end. Buxton (1946) described it as 'a loud scream, not unlike that of a peewit [Lapwing] but with the accent on the second instead of the first syllable' and as 'the wildest sound to be heard on the marshes...not musical but it gives me intense pleasure' Writers differ as to the rhythm of the call, whether it is uttered at the apex or upturn of the undulating display flight. My experience is that it is more irregular than that.

The alarm call, such as that made by the female when put up from the nest, is a 'kek-kek-kek-kek...' chatter or whicker, very much in the style of other harriers. The similar call of the male is lower in pitch. Cramp and Simmons (1980) describe the call of the female to the male from the nest as a 'thin plaintive-sounding "beeyuh", "bee" etc.'.

The male calls the female from the nest for a food-pass with a chuckling-type call, 'uck-uck-uck'. When the female or young solicit for food, they use an importuning repeated whistle, 'psee-oo', rather thin and more whinnying from the young, and quite undignified for an imposing raptor.

Breeding display

The high-flying climbing and tumbling displays of the harriers, evocatively termed 'skydancing' by Frances Hamerstrom (1969), are quite simply astounding. Words such as 'ecstacy', 'trance' and 'abandoned' occur in their description. Diving displays are not exclusive to the harriers, but the vigour

In spring, the skydancing diving display is mainly performed by the male.

and repetition in the displays executed by the genus are remarkable. Writers have grappled with the description of their display since Montagu (1802) remarked of the Marsh Harrier: 'in the breeding season, when the female is setting, the male will soar to a considerable height, and remain suspended on wing for a great length of time'.

Fine, sunny spring mornings are the prime time for skydancing, and warming air rising does allow the birds to circle up without much effort, but in the unpredictable weather of early spring brief display can take place on any day when conditions are not too adverse. Most display takes place in March and April, but I have seen it performed as late as the end of June. Soaring up perhaps hundreds of metres in circles with outstretched wings thrown forward in full soar, the male may feint once or twice, momentarily drawing in his wings as if hinting at the aerobatics about to begin. Then beating up further on stiffly outstretched wings to reach his wide sky arena, the intensity of his spring mood does vary. The less intense displays have the

63

character of careering about the sky, but not quite madly. Once the desired height has been reached, the pattern is one of a series of peaks. He climbs up nearly vertically each time, often helped by the force of pulling himself up against the breeze. Then beating his way to the top, he flashes his light underwings in the sun as he throws himself over at the apex of each climb. He beats his wings in a slow, deep flapping mode throughout both the steep ascent and generally a more gradual descent. This type of display, where a virtually even height is maintained across the peaks of the harrier's trajectory, is known as 'switchback', after the undulating rides on funfairs. The display may last for 10 or 15 minutes. He gives vent to the single, far-carrying scream at irregular intervals or more regularly during his manoeuvres. Following a prolonged performance of a high bird that is tiny in 10 x binoculars and moving perhaps a kilometre across a bright sky is not exactly comfortable for the observer, but it is very special and every spring I feel that each displaying harrier takes a little piece of my soul with it across the heavens. Monitoring them for long periods is difficult, and in misty conditions impossible – only the penetrating calling can be heard at intervals.

The male's descent from his sky arena is a diving display. Holding his wings in and perhaps coming almost all the way down in a quite uncomplicated manner, he slices through the air with a rushing sound that is quite audible if you are close enough. Alternatively, he dives down but pulls up into the wind at a number of stages on the way in a 'dropped-leaf' display, flipping over at the apex of each descendent peak and flashing his light underside. He might loop the loop once as he approaches the ground or swing from side to side; the aim seems to be to draw the attention of a female to the platform on to which he drops; she often joins him there. His swoops and flips may continue all the way down as he disappears into the reeds. At times he goes crazy, mixing and exaggerating all his moves, rolling, spinning and tumbling, and at the most extreme looking totally out of control.

I have also seen female Marsh Harriers skydance, but far less often and less vigorously. The 'dropped-leaf' display is more normal for them, without any intricate aerobatics; as they descend closer to the earth, their broader wings swing them this way and that in a lumbering stall and the limits on their manoeuvrability can be appreciated. Female participation in skydancing was not recorded for the Marsh Harrier according to Cramp and Simmons (1980), but they appear to have overlooked that Thiollay (1970) described it in the Camargue, where he recorded the male as displaying first in 90 per cent of cases and the female breaking into a display as the male dived down to the nest. More recently, in central Spain, female Marsh Harriers were noted to display as much as males by Blanco *et al.* (1993), who suggest that this is normal in the south of the range where the population (especially, in their experience, the females) is more sedentary; farther north, they maintain, the males are generally the first to return to breeding sites and perform the display, and there cannot be the incentive for females to get involved when territory is already delineated.

The sight of several skydancing Marsh Harriers competing has been rare in Britain. The presence of others does stimulate display, and in places where the breeding density is high many birds can interact. In the Camargue,

Thiollay saw up to six birds displaying out of thirteen in the sky, and in Australia Baker-Gabb (1983) recorded up to eight male Swamp Harriers in diving display at the same time. One of my favourite passages about sky-dancing is by Sharland (1932), who successfully conveys the strong impression made on him by the high density of Swamp Harriers in Tasmania in the early years of this century: 'The aerial evolutions of these hawks over the open space of the lake attracted our attention. I was not a little suprised to see them high in the sky, soaring, falling, twisting and turning, and resembling a number of flies. Whatever the cause, the performance was fine for us to watch, and we lay full length on the slope of the lake shore the better to see it. With the speed of a bolt from the sky a bird would dive headlong towards the expanse of rushes below, and when about half-way down, as if thinking it had exceeded the limit of respectable speed, would level out and in a few seconds, impelled by nothing but the momentum it had gained by the drop, shoot into the sky for 100 feet or so whence it had come. When its upward speed slackened it would remain poised for an instant, and slowly turning its head toward the earth, continue its giddy dive, only to repeat the swing and ascent again and again, till it reached the swamp beneath and landed in the thickness of the reed some distance from shore. Everywhere we looked the birds were engaged in this curious performance, and their shrill cries, uttered only on the upward flight after each great drop, came clearly to our ears. Harriers were continually rising from all parts of the lake to fill the places in the sky vacated by those just landed, and so the game went on all day till the sun got down towards the hills'.

In my experience, the display period of males of isolated pairs of Marsh Harriers is all too brief and easily missed. In semi-colonies, display diminishes over the breeding cycle, rarely being performed after incubation is over.

In an intensive study of the African Marsh Harrier, Simmons (1991a) described distinct 'sky-dancing' and 'sky-spiralling' displays. Jones (1989) illustrated skydancing well for one observation of display by the Réunion Harrier: it is a more horizontal performance of a series of undulations, either deep or quite shallow, and not necessarily executed at any great altitude; the wings are partly drawn in and held quite loosely, adding to an impression of almost a state of trance. Simmons' 'sky-spiralling' conforms to the 'dropped-leaf' type of display seen in *aeruginosus*, where the bird ascends to a great height and dives down in stages, also with loosely held wings, and while performing acrobatics of types including twisting on its axis (spiralling). The stages are marked by pulling up and losing all speed prior to each headlong dive, much in the manner of a falling leaf, and at the lower stages the bird may swing from side to side almost aimlessly on its large wings as it loses momentum, exactly like a leaf, and can give the appearance of loss of control.

The apparent trajectory described by sky dancing harriers can vary greatly, depending on the observer's position. Watched from the side, it appears to rise and fall in an even vertical plane. From behind or in front, as the bird progresses towards or away from the observer, the pattern described is often a coil or spiral. This has been described for the Réunion Harrier (Barré and Barau 1982) and was first pointed out by Frances Hamerstrom for the Northern Harrier.

Courting birds may 'toy and cuff', presenting their talons to each other in play.

Whether skydancing is a territorial or a courtship display, or both, is perhaps a moot point, but it is most certainly a strenuous performance and clearly requires a certain peak in condition to be executed well and repeatedly. Witkowski (1989) noted sky dancing by unpaired males, or in the presence of other males, as a prelude to more direct action if the others continued to intrude. In Canada, Simmons (1988a) established that the polygynous male Northern Harriers performing the most displays attracted the most mates. In South Africa, he experimented with supplementary feeding and found that African Marsh Harrier skydancing was linked to food abundance, which indicates that females which choose a mate on the basis of his excellence at skydancing would be choosing a male for his provisioning powers. species. He also found that males in stable monogamous relationships displayed as much as other males, suggesting that the display contained a strong territorial component rather than a simply mate-attracting function.

The form of display probably has an important role in mate recognition within the species. Differences between the displays of harrier species are not well documented, and would repay an extensive study recording and comparing the moves in a standardized notation.

Some courtship moves involve the male playfully diving on the female in the air, she flipping over to present talons. Jardine's words 'toy and cuff' come to mind from the description of the Hen Harrier's courtship in his edition of Wilson's 1821 *American Ornithology*. More determined chasing can be seen, but often the exact identity of the protagonists – whether or not they are mates – cannot be established at a busy reedbed in early spring. As in much animal display, physical contact is rare.

The male Marsh Harrier in particular will fly about, extensively, low over the reedbed in early spring, planing very slowly into the March or April breeze with hardly a flap, hesitating over some places with a series of bursts of very shallow wingbeats, rounding into the wind to check his progress and minutely examine the reedbed beneath him, settling down into it every now and again. This minute searching of intended breeding territory is clearly important to harriers.

The food-pass

As the incoming male approaches, the prey in his talons is normally visible as his legs are dropped; if it is a small item, it may be tucked up with his feet under the tail and the legs dropped only for the pass. He calls the female off the nest with a subdued chuckle of a call; the female leaves, gaining some height and flying towards or after him, and either the two land to transfer on the ground, or the male passes the food to the female in the air. Aerial food-passes are variable in the elegance of their execution. In the classic type, unfortunately the rarest, the female flies right up to the male and rears over in mid-air to take the food directly from his talons, in the process turning completely upside-down immediately underneath him as their talons meet. I have seen this move appear absolutely magical in the slow-motion of a film. In real life it is more fleeting. More commonly, the food is dropped a short distance as the female approaches and she banks or rears up to catch it in outstretched talons. The male often sweeps up at the last moment to give the prey some momentum counter to gravity as he drops it, thereby slowing its speed of fall. The pass has all the elements of good theatre – anticipation, suspense, climax – and often leaves one wanting more; the final act is almost too fast for the eye to follow. The female will often not return to the nest directly, but may take the prey to a resting place, perhaps to eat it or to prepare it before flying back low to the nest.

Aerial food-passing is used by all the harriers. It avoids the risk of interference on the ground by mammals and other birds and is convenient for birds so skilled in flight. The number of catches missed is neglible – 6 (3.5 per cent) out of 169 between adult Marsh Harriers (Fernández and Azkona 1994a) and 0–4 per cent in adult harrier passes elsewhere (Simmons 1991b). Inexperienced young are of course less adept at catching from adults. The proportion of food-passes made in flight has been shown to increase during the nestling phase and to be greater at nest with higher brood sizes. (Fernádez ad Azkona 1994a). This may be as a result of intensifying demand behaviour by the female.

The avoidance of visits to the nest by the incoming male may protect the young from his heightened hunting instinct; also, the nest's location is not so obvious since it is far more difficult to pinpoint the spot from where the female rises than it is to follow the descent of the male bearing prey and the more activity is kept away from the nest the better. The female's later return to the nest is more low-key and inconspicuous.

Polygyny

Polygyny occurs far more frequently in harriers than in other raptors. A number of theories have been put forward as to why. For the Hen Harrier, Picozzi (1984) suggested that the advantage to females was that more were able to breed in the situation on Orkney, where there appeared to be a short-age of males. Also, polygynous males were more likely to rear young, and reared more young on average, than monogamous males. In a situation of a more even sex ratio, there would appear to be little benefit to females, but males get the chance of producing more young from their genes. For the Northern Harrier, Simmons (1989) showed that females in polygynous relationships reared fewer young. He suggested that males acquire females by deception, in that they provide well in the courtship stages but do not maintain this. One female (the 'primary' or 'alpha' female) normally takes precedence by being the first female to begin breeding and the polygynous male usually keeps her nest much better supplied with food. Simmons did find, however, that the incidence of polygyny was related to abundance of food. In birds such as harriers, which exploit the rich, early stages of habit at succession, polygyny may be an opportunistic occurrence where males can provide more than one mate requires. Where females recognize that this may be the case, they may prefer a polygynous relationship to a monogamous one elsewhere in a poorer territory.

Polygyny has been widely reported for the Marsh Harrier, but anything more than bigamy is extremely rare. The Marsh Harrier's larger size may make the food demands of two females more difficult to meet than in other species of harrier. Hen Harrier harems of up to six females were found by Balfour and Cadbury (1979) on Orkney, with the larger harems attaching to the more mature males. Sach (1967) reported an exceptional instance of polygyny in the Marsh Harrier in the far north of Germany: two adult pairs laid at the beginning of May, but on 23 May a group of four young females appeared and proceeded to take prey from the two males and to nest; one male fed three females and the other fed five!

It can be difficult to prove polygyny in the field, especially with a number of nests in an area. It also appears to be more prevalent in certain regions. Schipper (1979) found a very high rate of polygyny in Flevoland (16 out of 28 nests, or 57 per cent), whereas in the nearby Weerribben only four out of 171 nests were polygynous (Woets 1989). Elsewhere it was often rare – less than 4 per cent of 258 nests in Poland (Witkowski 1989). González found that it was rare in central Spain, as did Jørgensen in Denmark.

The principal study of polygyny in the Marsh Harrier is that by Altenburg *et al.* (1982) in the Netherlands. At 421 nests found in the Lauwersmeer and Flevoland, 156 were *known* to have been monogamous, 30 males were known to be bigamous and one was trigamous. Comparing the results of monogamous and bigamous nests in a fast-growing new

A number of birds can be seen gathering to roost communally at favoured sites in autumn.

population in the Lauwersmeer polder, they found that bigamous males reared almost twice as many young as did monogamous males, but their primary females were more successful than secondary females, with higher mortality in secondary nests. More prey deliveries were made by bigamous males. Predictably, polygynous females began hunting at an earlier stage and also delivered prey to the nest at a greater rate than did monogamous females.

Underhill-Day (1984) noted an increase in the rate of polygyny in Britain (11 per cent of nests in 1945–58, 23 per cent in 1959–71, 32 per cent in 1972–82), and such nests fledged more young than monogamous nests, perhaps indicating that territories were generally of a high quality. About 15 per cent of breeding males in Britain now have more than one mate (Underhill-Day in Gibbons *et al.* 1993). In Flevoland, Schipper (1979) also found that both primary and secondary polygynous nests were more successful. Witkowski recorded lower success for both primary and secondary nests in the few polygynous relationships occurring in his study area, although the production of young per male was still higher.

Communal roosting

Communal roosting outside the breeding season is known to occur in all species of harrier apart from the Spotted Harrier, about which little is known in winter. The African Marsh Harrier, which is mate-specific and remains on territory the year round (Simmons *in litt.*), has not been recorded roosting communally in recent times, but Gurney (1868) noted evening 'congregations' of up to thirty.

The birds often begin to gather from an hour or so before sunset on some convenient bare surface close to the site, standing facing into the breeze, preening and looking around. Where no suitable surface presents itself, in a large reedbed for example, they will perch on bushes. Little interaction takes place. From about sunset they will begin to leave the pre-roost

or arrive from elsewhere to prospect the roost site. Generally, this is an area of rank ground vegetation. They settle individually on flattened, surrounded by a protective wall of the vegetation. They tend to roost in loose groups, favouring one part of the reedbed or field. The preferred area changes from time to time, but certain places are traditional, being used winter after winter when the vegetation there is right. Before settling a number of birds are often in the air at the same time, and with larger numbers there appears to be an intensity of activity, of flying to and fro over the site and displacing each other from roosting places.

The dispersal in the morning begins soon after first light but is not immediate. Birds will leave their roosting form and many settle at a short distance to preen. They gradually disperse widely over the neighbourhood and beyond.

At places along the English coast from Lincolnshire to Kent, the blowsy, utilitarian landscape of arable farmland at harvest is the theatre for autumn communal roosts of juvenile and post-breeding adult Marsh Harriers. Gatherings of more than 30 birds have been recorded in north Norfolk, more than 20 in Lincolnshire and up to 15 on the Isle of Sheppey in Kent (Hadrill 1991). Growing in size in August and early September, north Norfolk roosts can disappear almost overnight in mid September, as the instinct to migrate takes hold. On Sheppey, the composition of adults, sub adults and juveniles fluctuates significantly from night to night in late August and early September, indicating that passage birds are involved, although some well-marked individuals have been recorded throughout the period. Early evening sees the harriers gathering at pre-roost on stubble or ploughed land. There is some social interaction – an individual already present will often fly out to meet a new arrival. The harriers move in after sunset, settling in the crop. As the harvest progresses, the harriers are faced with a diminishing choice. One memorable evening in west Norfolk, I watched from a vantage point on an old sea wall as juvenile harriers flew in one at a time to settle on a ploughed field adjoining the last stand of wheat. A trio of yellow-painted combine harvesters toiled up and down, whittling away at the wheat and frequently pausing to unload. An adult male, recognizable as from a local nest, flew into the pre-roost, but was immediately hustled out by a juvenile following him in. The male flew away to the north and the juveniles scattered, soon to reassemble on stubble left by the early work of the harvesters. One flew over and settled in the crop, but came out quickly as three harvesters bore down on it. An adult female with large yellow semi circles on her forewings arrived from the south and settled with the pre-roost. The harriers were soon in the air, settling in the crop as the harvesters headed for the far end of the field. The male reappeared from the north, several harriers jumping up momentarily as he flew over the crop. He was soon off south as the juveniles fled the roost, with the harvesters turning back on them. They settled on the stubble momentarily, but then several were again flying above the crop, silhouettes against the lights of the nearby seaside resort. The light was fast fading and a Short-eared Owl appeared, sparring

Comparitive studies of adult female, ginger-capped juvenile and all-dark juvenile Marsh Harriers.

with two of the harriers high above the roost. Observation soon became impossible, and I could only guess at the harriers' eventual roosting place as the harvesters worked towards a finish by headlamp light.

Winter communal roosts of Marsh Harriers form at a handful of sites in Britain, in Norfolk, Suffolk and Kent. The radio-tracking of juveniles by Bavoux *et al.* (1992) showed that birds from their largely sedentary population in France used up to eight different roosts in a winter.

The function of pre-roosting remains a mystery. It appears to be linked to the photoperiod, and the pre-roost perhaps acts as a staging post and resting place for birds arriving too early to indulge immediately in milling above the roost itself. It seems to assist in coordination of roosting activity. I once observed an interesting segregation of species at a pre-roost on the edge of a saltmarsh in the Gulf of Kutch in Gujarat, north-west India: Marsh Harriers were flying over from a nearby freshwater lagoon and settled either on bare patches of mud between sea-blite bushes or along a dyke bordering the saltmarsh; the roost itself was farther out towards the sea, and comprised a mix of harrier species; none of the Montagu's or Pallid Harriers present joined the pre-roost. Gurr (1968) described some quite elaborate interaction by New Zealand Swamp Harriers at pre-roost, including individuals flying up to chase a new arrival up to about 30 m and for two or three minutes, stimulating other birds to join in. He also recorded the first courtship displays there, by solitary birds, just before the breeding season.

Roosts can become quite large. For example, autumn congregations on saltmarsh at one site in the south-west Netherlands exceed 100 individuals, although they are very spread out over the marsh, in contrast to the tight grouping in midwinter of up to about 30 birds roosting there. In southern Spain the Marismas del Guadalquivir is clearly an important wintering site, with up to 210 Marsh Harriers recorded at a roost (Gonzalez 1991). Some really large roosts of up to 300 harriers have occurred in the past in New Zealand (Stead 1932).

Mobbing by other species

Being relatively slow in flight, the harriers tend to be mobbed more often than other raptors. The species that perhaps mob the Marsh Harrier the hardest are the waders of the marsh edge – Lapwings and Redshanks, complete with the evocative sound of their sentient alarm calls. A harrier will show great agility by rolling over in an instant to present talons to the assailants diving on it. Sometimes it will be carrying prey, though, and will try to ignore the attacks. Some interesting questions arise concerning mobbing. Bilstein (1982) examined these, mainly with reference to the Northern Harrier in the USA. He found that harriers were not mobbed when perched, but only when flying, and that this intensified significantly (they were six times more likely to be mobbed) if the harrier was carrying prey. Mobbing by small passerines is not really a problem unless, of course, the latter are in great numbers.

8

TERRITORIAL BEHAVIOUR

The numerical strength of the Marsh Harrier breeding population pivots on the capacity of available marshland, a scarce resource. Spatial strategy is therefore highly important for this species. Harriers in general tend to nest in clumps or 'semi-colonies' but hunt individually, ranging out extensively over surrounding land. This arrangement effectively maximizes the capacity of scarce nesting habitat. The Hen Harrier and Montagu's Harrier also breed in marshes, but not nearly as exclusively so as the Marsh Harrier, and the tendency of Hen Harriers, for example, to nest in semi-colonies in one area of a wide tract of seemingly uniform moorland habitat indicates that there may be some additional factor to clumping. The basing of non-breeding activities on a communal roost site is a similar spatial arrangement used by most harriers, but winter communal roosts are also known in solitarily nesting species of raptor.

Breeding density seems to be less in the Marsh Harrier than in the smaller Hen and Montagu's, perhaps as a result of its larger size and more restricted habitat preferences which limit numbers and require greater spacing of nesting pairs, especially in the early stages when the birds spend more time in the breeding marsh. Breeding density, however, can be as high as a mean inter-nest distance of 100 m (Berg and Stiefel 1968), in effect a loose colony. Witkowski (1989) recorded a mean annual density of down to 26.5 ha per pair within the area used by Marsh Harriers for nesting, with a mean distance of 210 m between nests in the wider reedbeds along the shore. In the Czech Republic and Slovakia, Danko et al (1994) found that marsh habitat was used very intensively in dry years, with nests often only a few tens of metres apart.

During the courtship and incubation periods, activity is concentrated on the breeding marsh. Territory size is at this stage typically small – a radius of 100–300 m around the nest – and the male spends a lot of time in early spring patrolling this and defending it against all perceived enemies such as crows and predatory mammals. The defence of territory against rivals varies in intensity, eliciting responses varying from threatening to escorting and to attacking. Moles are the most frequent defenders of territory against other Marsh Harrier but they are more tolerant of female intruders early in the season (Fernández and Azkora 1994b). Behaviour involving actual contact is rare. Escorting takes the form of following, chasing or 'pushing' the intruder up or away out of territorial airspace. Flying with legs lowered is a form of threat used to maintain territorial boundaries and if possible to avoid potentially damaging contact. This was reviewed in various territorial predatory

Territorial males push rivals up and away in an escorting flight from behind and below. Fights are rare.

birds by Barnard and Simmons (1986). Occasionally, this demonstration will escalate into a fight, and, as in play, an attacked bird's reaction is to flip over and present talons, and rarely the two will actually grasp each other by the talons and fall to the ground. Observing this in the African Marsh Harrier, Simmons (1991a) recorded that 'these encounters lasted 1–7 minutes, while the birds were presumed fighting or locked together on the ground'. At Horsey, Buxton found that some male Marsh Harriers were particularly pugnacious and one year he found the corpse of the first male to arrive in spring floating in the dyke under its preening post, 'no doubt slain by his rival who apparently lost a wing feather in the process'.

Once the young are hatched, the males abruptly extend their activities beyond the nesting territory by making long foraging flights into surrounding, often marginal or arable, land. The reason for this is very clear. Unless a particularly rich source of waterfowl is available, marshland hunting is not very productive. At Titchwell in one season, Sills (1983) observed that it took a male an average of 27 minutes to catch prey in the marsh, and it was likely to be a small item such as a fledgling passerine; prey was caught every 17 minutes on average on farmland and was usually a much heavier young Pheasant, Rabbit or Starling. Sills calculated that farmland was ten times more productive in terms of weight of food per minute of hunting. Elsewhere in East Anglia, Underhill-Day (1989) established that the size of the hunting range of a male was very much larger during the nestling stage than it was earlier or later.

The males tend to hunt sectors of the compass based on their nest. Some researchers have found that such hunting territory is defended against other Marsh Harriers (Sondell 1970). Others maintain that it is not unusual for the hunting ranges of neighbouring males to overlap and that hunting territories are not defended.

How far might a harrier range from the nest? Maximum hunting distances from nests by male Marsh Harriers were recorded by Schipper *et al.* (1977) in Holland and France at only 1.5 to 3.1 km, females ranging only 1.4 to 1.8 km; they quoted other researchers as recording 5–8 km. In Cambridgeshire, where nesting pairs have had no near neighbours, I had one observation of the Wicken Fen male well away from the nest: one lunch-hour in 1985, at about the end of the harriers' incubation period I spotted him coursing low over the reeds of a marsh 12 km south of Wicken; he soon circled up in the sunshine and made off south, away from Wicken! There was no doubt that it was he – the same two inner primaries missing with no sign of regrowth and one or two tail feathers cut off short (shot damage acquired on migration?). On a separate occasion he was seen at another marsh 10 km east of Wicken.

The sizes of hunting ranges quoted by Schipper *et al.* vary from 250 to 680 ha for males and 80 to 370 ha for females. At Titchwell, hunting ranges out over arable farmland, inland of the coastal breeding marsh, were measured for individual males in 1982 and 1983 at a much larger 1250 ha and 1000 ha respectively (Sills 1988). Elsewhere in East Anglia, Underhill-Day (1989) calculated 217 ha during the courtship stage, 170 ha during incubation, 1112 ha during the nestling period and 310 ha during the fledgling period. In Poland, Witkowski (1989) calculated a far smaller mean area of 125 ha of arable fields and meadow plus 35 ha of fishpond used by each pair in a large semi-colony, with up to 50 pairs using 80 km^2. It seems clear that, so far as range sizes go, it all depends on the habitat, prey density and the stage of the breeding cycle.

9

MOVEMENTS AND WINTERING AREAS

Much of the emphasis of bird study is on breeding, but knowledge of the factors affecting birds during the 'internuptial' period (as the French so aptly put it) is also vital. Marsh Harriers spend about five months on their breeding-grounds. It could therefore be argued that many studies look at less than half the picture. The birds are at high risk during migration and may be affected by many unknown factors on the wintering-grounds, such as harmful pesticides.

Marsh Harriers arrive on their breeding-grounds north of the main wintering range from mid March to early May, depending on latitude (Glutz von Blotzheim *et al.* 1971). In northerly breeding areas, the melting of the ice gripping the wetlands in winter may be a factor. Witkowski (1989) recorded Marsh Harriers in some years returning before the ice melted, making use of meadows and arable fields for hunting until the marsh had thawed.

Migratory populations in the north of Europe begin to disperse in the second half of August (Witkowski 1989), moving through the northern Netherlands for example at that time and with smaller numbers in September and early October (Bijlsma 1993). In England, the majority appear to remain in their natal area well into September, but then most leave fairly suddenly. The abrupt exodus is likely to be linked to prey availability. In former times, Marsh Harriers would probably have relied much more on cold-blooded prey, amphibians such as frogs for example. As these become less active and young, inexperienced bird prey is no longer available, the necessity to move south must become urgent.

Dispersal from breeding-grounds

The extent of migration depends on latitude. Marsh Harriers breeding north of the most northerly wintering-grounds in the Netherlands and England, and from the great majority of central and eastern Europe, where cold winters typify the climate, are entirely migratory. Birds originating from breeding areas within the wintering range have the choice of being sedentary or migratory. Ringing recoveries confirm that some Marsh Harriers in western and southern Europe remain close to their natal areas in winter, and there is evidence that adult females more often choose to remain in the breeding area. The intensive study of local movements of birds requires the use of radio-tracking. So far, the only such study has been undertaken by Bavoux *et al.* (1992), on young birds. They found that at least 63 per cent of young bred in their study area in western France were sedentary, with no significant difference between the sexes. There may be a tendency for juveniles to be less migratory than adults. Study of a winter roost in the south of the Netherlands, close to the northerly limit of the winter range, showed that it was used mainly by juveniles (Clarke *et al.* 1993). It is almost certain that the choice of strategy is related to the availability of prey of the right size in sufficient density. The general tendency is to migrate to the south-west. Also, birds from the most northerly breeding-grounds tend to travel the furthest south, overtaking birds from lower latitudes during migration. Of 25 foreign recoveries of birds from Finland noted by Hildén and Kalinainen (1966), only one occurred in the midwinter period of November to January, on the east coast of Spain; six others, mainly in August–October, were in Italy or the south of France, and three in February–April comprised one in Africa (south of the Sahara, in the north of Cameroon) and two crossing the Mediterranean.

The route south has been clearly established from ringing recoveries. For example, Marsh Harriers ringed in north-west Germany (Zang *et al.* 1989; Looft and Busche 1990) have been recovered very largely in a corridor running south-west through the Netherlands, Belgium, northern, central and southern France and down the east coast of Spain, into Morocco and as far as West Africa. A very few of the recoveries are of birds which appear to have chosen the central route across the Mediterranean, down through Italy. This pattern appears to be fairly typical of west European populations. For British-ringed birds, Mead (1973) published a review of recoveries up to 1970 (for the 127 ringed to that date) and showed a very similar pattern, with just three foreign recoveries: in northern France, Morocco, and south of the Sahara in Mauritania. Of six foreign recoveries since then (a further 464 birds were ringed to the end of 1991), one youngster from the 1985 nest at Wicken Fen was also found in Mauritania, on 1 October in that year; three Minsmere birds were recovered in Portugal (one) and Morocco (two), and single Lincolnshire and Suffolk birds in north-west Spain. Foreign-ringed birds recovered in Britain have come from Denmark, Germany, Holland and Belgium.

Recoveries of Marsh Harriers ringed in eastern Europe show many on a south-west route in the south of France, along the east side of Spain and into Morocco. There is then a gap across the Sahara and a few recoveries in West Africa. A significant number of recoveries, however, occur in the north of Italy, and single ones in Corsica and Sardinia probably indicate a west-central route across the Mediterranean; a number take the east-central route and are recovered in the south of Italy and at the Strait of Messina. Central-route birds are also recovered in Tunisia and west from there along the north coast of Africa (Ilyichew 1982). Marsh Harriers ringed at Cap Bon have been recovered in Poland, Czechoslovakia, the former USSR, Romania and Cyprus (Thomsen and Jacobsen 1979).

Data showing the dispersal of Asian Marsh Harriers are lacking, but the lack of recoveries of European individuals in east Africa suggests that those occurring there in winter are from western Asia.

MAP 2 *Winter ranges of the three migratory Marsh Harriers.*

Migration

Their light wing-loading frees the harriers from reliance on warm-air thermals, allowing them to be active in cold early-morning air and to make long sea crossings on migration.

Harriers in general migrate singly or in very small loose groups, and on a broad front using flapping flight. However, they probably use up more energy than the broad-winged raptors such as buzzards that use overland thermals and therefore avoid long sea crossings. Independent of thermals, harriers tend to move earlier in the day than other raptors. There is also some evidence that they can migrate at night, individuals having been recorded arriving at Malta at dawn after a long sea crossing in unfavourable weather (Clark in Newton 1990). Finlayson (1991) observed that, despite their broad-front abilities, Marsh Harriers often behaved in a way similar to that of soaring birds, for example struggling to reach the Rock of Gibraltar when blown east of it by strong westerly winds in spring, rather than striking out north for the Spanish coast; they tended to drift west or east with the prevailing wind.

The most concentrated harrier migration in the world is that of Pied and Eastern Marsh Harriers at Beidaihe on the east coast of China, where birds

Harriers migrate singly or in very small groups on a wide front and are not dependent on short sea crossings.

moving in autumn through the valleys of the eastern Asian mountains and across the lowlands of Manchuria funnel down through the narrow strip of land between Beijing and the coast. Counts run into many thousands.

In Britain, the principal Marsh Harrier migration route is along the east coast of England, although some migrants are recorded on the south coast, too. Passage is more noticeable in spring, beginning in earnest in late April or early May. Many of these birds must be non-breeders or travelling farther north, since most Marsh Harriers breeding along the east coast of England arrive rather earlier, in the second half of March or the first half of April.

The most famous raptor migration point in northern Europe is at Falsterbo at the very south-western tip of Sweden, where the birds concentrate to make the short sea crossing south to Denmark. Although the hundreds of harriers do not come close to matching the thousands of Common Buzzards, Honey Buzzards and Sparrowhawks counted migrating through Falsterbo each autumn, the data yield some interesting facts. Over the seven autumns 1986–92, peak passage of Marsh Harriers generally occurred in the last two-thirds of August and the first third of September, although sometimes it continued strongly later into September. Adult males consistently came through slightly later than females and juveniles. Juveniles greatly outnumbered adults, as might be expected after the breeding season, and females dominated among the adults (Kjellén 1993).

Farther south, at Organbidexxa and nearby sites in the French Pyrenees, where thousands of Honey Buzzards and kites are the most numerous raptor migrants, the Marsh Harrier also concentrates in very modest numbers. For example, the 1993 autumn count was 339, peaking sharply on 19–20 September. At Monte Conero in north-east Italy, on the Adriatic coast, the Marsh Harrier is one of the commonest migrant raptors in spring: in 1987–90, they occurred throughout the period from late March to early May, with up to 932 counted in a season, and exceeded Honey Buzzards in number in both 1989 and 1990 (Borioni 1993).

Many Marsh Harriers probably cross the Mediterranean on a broad front. The numbers recorded using the western and eastern flyways are tiny compared with the many thousands of broad-winged raptors. On the central flyway, however, they appear to form a larger proportion of the total migrant raptors. Logically, the south-westerly bias of the migration of European birds would appear to lead many of them to cross in the far west, at the Strait of Gibraltar, but counts of Marsh Harriers there are not high, amounting to 200–400 each autumn compared with many thousands of Honey Buzzards (Bernis 1980). Marsh Harriers are, however, particularly difficult to count there because they tend to migrate singly and often at a fair height, using the wider reaches of the Strait as much as the narrower crossing (Finlayson 1991). Crossing takes place from mid August to the beginning of September and the return from the end of February to the beginning of May, with no significant difference in numbers between autumn and spring. Adult males predominate earlier in spring.

Passage through the central Mediterranean flyway between Cap Bon at the north-eastern tip of Tunisia, Malta and the Strait of Messina, between Sicily and the toe of Italy, is stronger in spring. The Marsh Harrier is the second commonest migrant raptor there after the Honey Buzzard. Counts between 31 March and 3 June 1990 totalled 978, and again birds in adult male plumage migrate earlier (Giordano 1991).

Few migrant Marsh Harriers are recorded at the eastern end of the Mediterranean, crossing the Bosphorus, but counts in Israel of birds which probably come mostly out of Asia, down between the Black and Caspian seas, are comparable with those on the west and central flyways. At Eilat in southernmost Israel, statistics show up to 371 (1983) counted on spring migration from the second week in March to the second week in May and peak numbers on days ranging from 3 April to 3 May; autumn numbers of migrating raptors there are much smaller, up to 75 Marsh Harriers (1987) from mid October to mid November (Shirihai and Christie 1992). Farther north, at Kefar Kassim on the Mediterranean coastal plain inland from Tel-Aviv, counts have been higher, up to 1237 in autumn (Dovrat 1991), and in the Northern Valleys in the autumn up to 1534 (Tsovel and Allon 1991). Farther west, at Suez, Bijlsma (1983) recorded only 35 Marsh Harriers between 13 September and 2 October in 1981, remarking on their lack of a need to use short sea crossings. Very few move down through Saudi Arabia to enter east Africa across the Bab-el-Mandeb strait at Djibouti, (Welch and Welch 1988).

In New Zealand, the Swamp Harrier is rather sedentary, with ringing recoveries showing adults remaining in the same areas and juveniles dispersing up to a few hundred miles. The highest altitude recorded for a migrating harrier was over 1200 m, witnessed by a pilot in New Zealand (Black 1957). In Australia, the Swamp Harrier breeds only in the southwest, the south-east and in Tasmania. Australia is large enough to provide sufficient climatic variation to contain most seasonal movement within its limits. Large numbers leave Tasmania for the Australasian winter

(Sharland 1958; Hobbs 1959), these, along with others that breed in the south-east, moving up the east coast of Australia, with a few reaching Papua New Guinea, where they occur with the resident Papuan Harrier (Coates 1985). Swamp Harriers in the south-west of Australia are not known to be migratory (Baker-Gabb and Fitzherbert 1989).

Wintering areas

As the west European population has recovered, there has been an increasing trend for Marsh Harriers, mostly adult females and juveniles, to winter in a few places in north-west Europe. This is not 'new', since the species was recorded as a resident in some old English county avifaunas. Wintering in north-west Europe, however, appears to have largely ceased while the species was at its lowest ebb.

The wintering range of *aeruginosus* in the west of the Old World stretches from England and the Netherlands down to southern Africa; in the east, it extends throughout the Indian subcontinent down to Sri Lanka and even farther east through Burma and the Malayan peninsula to Sumatra. The northern boundary of the species' wintering range, stretches across Europe from East Anglia, the Netherlands and Belgium, taking in the west and the south of France, skirting south of the Alps in northern Italy, and from there eastwards to take in only the very southern extremities of Europe. This line closely matches the 0°C winter isotherm.

Wintering sites in the Netherlands and England are based on large marshes, rivers or lakes where there is no shortage of food, usually where significant numbers of Marsh Harriers have bred and close to the coast, where the effects of frost would be less severe. In the Camargue, Schipper *et al.* (1975) noted a sudden exodus of Marsh Harriers in frosty weather. Even carrion is of little use if it is frozen. The smaller breeding sites inland, rarely attract the species in winter. In the Norfolk Broads, Vincent first noted one wintering in 1937, a young female reared there the previous spring, and that locality is one of the best for wintering Marsh Harriers in Britain today, with up to nine (1990) recorded in midwinter at the principal roost. In the Broads, the wintering population in the early 1990s numbers 10–20 birds, and individuals have wintered on the North Norfolk coast, since 1984. Other wintering places are the Minsmere/Walberswick area of coastal Suffolk, where winter roosts of up to nine birds have been counted in the reedbeds, and the Isle of Sheppey in Kent (eight in 1993/94: P. Hadrill pers. comm.), and individuals frequent marshes such as Poole Harbour in Dorset and Kenfig Pool, Oxwich Marsh and Crymlyn Bog on the south coast of Wales from time to time. Single birds are occasional winter visitors to the south-west of England, the top sites being Marazion Marsh in Cornwall and Slapton Ley in Devon. The number wintering in Britain as a whole probably does not exceed 30. Two individuals have wintered in Wexford, in the south-eastern corner of Ireland (Hutchinson 1989).

In the Netherlands, Zijlstra (1987) mapped three wintering places, all large marshes. The most northerly of these was Flevoland, but in recent winters there have been no significant numbers of Marsh Harriers there. The

Marshland bushes can be favourite perches, in this case for a wintering bird at Bharatpur in India.

Haringvliet in south-west Holland is the next most northerly; it was dammed off from the sea in 1971, which encouraged much growth of reed and changed it from salt to fresh water, and it now contains a significant winter roost of Marsh Harriers. Zijlstra's third wintering site was just in-land from the Haringvliet, at Biesbos. In the far south-west of Holland, Saeftinghe is now also an important site, with a winter roost of up to thirty birds. Females and juveniles tend to predominate at these sites in winter, where waterfowl are the main food source. Males may be less able to win-ter so far north, because their smaller size gives them less ability to com-pete for carrion and less potential for killing waterfowl.

Central Europe retains few wintering Marsh Harriers. The massive Neusiedler See on the east Austrian border, with breeding habitat for up to some 70 pairs, regularly holds just single individuals in winter (Gamauf 1991).

In France, the winter distribution closely follows the breeding range apart from in the north where significant breeding areas in the marshes of Lorraine and Champagne are vacated. Although a few birds are found along the north coast, the main winter distribution stretches all down the west coast, ex-tending inland around the Loire and the Charente Maritime marshes and La Brenne. The other principal wintering area is along the Mediterranean coast, centred on the Rhône Delta and the Camargue (Yeatman-Berthelot 1991).

In view of the probable importance of Spain as a wintering area for Marsh Harriers from northern Europe, a nationwide coordinated count was carried out by the Grupo Iberico de Rapaces in 1990. The winter distribu-tion was found to match that in the breeding season, with the addition of a

82

An immature soaring in morning mist at Bharatpur. It shows the characteristic light bases to the primaries of a young brown Marsh Harrier, as opposed to the full sandy-coloured panel on the primaries of an adult female.

few areas, notably on the east Mediterranean coast at the Ebro Delta and La Albufera. The total counted was 1713. Since the population of breeding adults totals about 1000 birds, and juveniles would add considerably to this, the increase in numbers overall in Spain in winter would not appear to be great, and the birds present may be largely resident.

Wetlands in Africa and India are important wintering places.

Large numbers of Marsh Harriers winter in southern Europe, but a proportion crosses into Africa. Some winter in north-west Africa. Ringed birds recovered in Morocco have come mainly from the Netherlands and East Germany (Bergier 1987). Two British-ringed Marsh Harriers have been recovered south of the Sahara in Mauritania. Such trans-Saharan migrants use marshes, lakes, lagoons, rice fields and flooded grasslands in the savanna and semi-arid zones in a band south of the Sahara and north of the rainforest zone in the west and extending down into the plains of the east. The Sahelian floodplain of the Niger river supports perhaps thousands of Marsh Harriers from the Palearctic that depend on the abundant wildfowl there. Farther west, in Senegal, an area based around a section of the inundation zone of the Senegal river, visited in the 1992/93 winter by Arroyo and King (in press) was estimated to hold more than 1000 Marsh Harriers; two large roosts in rice fields each held 300–350 birds. By March they had virtually all left on migration.

The resident African harriers have very restricted distributions. The Black Harrier has the smallest range of any harrier, confined to the Republic of South Africa, parts of neighbouring Namibia and Botswana. The African Marsh Harrier occurs in the south and east. The winter ranges of the migrant Palearctic Marsh Harrier and the resident African Marsh Harrier overlap in Kenya, Uganda, Tanzania and Zambia. Occasionally the migrant Palearctic bird penetrates into Botswana, Zimbabwe, Mozambique or even the Transvaal, where exceptionally up to five were recorded on the Nyl river in the winter of 1987/88 (Simmons 1988b). Apart from a few individuals, however, the Marsh Harrier does not penetrate so far as the wholly long-haul migrant Montagu's and Pallid Harriers from Europe and western Asia, but all three have been scarce in southern Africa in recent decades, doubtless a consequence of reduced populations. They were more formerly prominent and, as Moreau (1972) remarked, 'compared to the Palearctic species during their stay the native African harriers can hardly be said to be "in business"'.

The coexistence of harrier species when breeding is complicated. The wintering situation can be even more so, the most extreme example being perhaps that of Marsh, Eastern Marsh, Montagu's, Pallid, Hen and Pied Harriers in north-east India, occurring at the same roosts. Throughout the Indian subcontinent, wintering Marsh Harriers coming from Asian breeding-grounds north of the Himalayas use open wetlands. These areas appear to contain much suitable breeding habitat, but lack any harrier species in the summer. In the east, in Assam and beyond, the Eastern Marsh Harrier, called the Striped Harrier in India, begins to replace *aeruginosus*, the two mixing in winter down through Burma, to Sumatra. The Eastern Marsh Harrier winters in suitable habitat throughout much of the rest of south-east Asia.

The Australian Swamp Harrier is partly migratory. Northern Australia is an important wintering area, but it has seen widescale agricultural development (Baker-Gabb and Fitzherbert 1989).

10

HUNTING AND PREY

Harriers are generalist predators that fly low and drop on any prey of a suitable size that can be surprised on the ground. This does not mean that they do not specialize, given the opportunity, but their specialization can range from locusts to ducks. It depends on the local abundance of the prey in question, the competition for it, and whether the structure of the habitat where it occurs is suited to the harriers' hunting technique. Where no one prey is particularly profitable, the diet can be very wide indeed. The diet of the Marsh Harrier is selected from insects, crustaceans, fish, amphibians, reptiles, birds and mammals. In Britain, prey size can vary from under 10 g (e.g. a Harvest Mouse) to more than 600 g (e.g. an adult duck), and larger animals are eaten as carrion. To close successfully on prey, the harrier uses stealth, adapting its flying speed and altitude to strike a compromise between an efficient search and being in a position to strike effectively. It uses the wind to mould its flight, and above all the structure of the vegetation to surprise prey. It is difficult for the Marsh Harrier to have any success with hunting over bare ground or low vegetation, where potential prey can see the harrier coming. In the breeding season it picks on the young and inexperienced as prey, but colonial birds such as terns and gulls, and other species such as waders and ducks out in the open, are generally too vigorous in defence of their young to allow the harrier to succeed. Of all the harriers, the Marsh Harrier is the most prone to feeding on carrion. Because its diet is selected from a wide spectrum of potential prey, the breeding success of the Marsh Harrier is rarely influenced by fluctuations in individual prey species in the way that, for example, raptors specializing on small mammals are affected by vole cycles.

Harriers hunt mostly by trying to surprise prey on the ground.

Adaptations

The light structure and long wings of the harriers are adaptations to prolonged searching on the wing. Wing-loading measurements (weight of bird divided by wing area) for the harriers are much lower than those for raptors of similar size other than the kites, which are also very aerial birds. Harriers range from about 0.21 g/cm^2 in the smaller species to 0.30 g/cm^2 in the Marsh Harrier (Brown and Amadon 1968). Even a relatively heavy harrier such as the Marsh Harrier has a far lower wing-loading than, for example, the Common Buzzard at 0.45 g/cm^2. The Marsh Harrier has a shorter tail and smaller flight apparatus than other harriers, in relation to body-weight. In the New Zealand Swamp Harrier, Fox (1977a) calculated wing loading at about 0.39 g/cm^2 in males and 0.41 g/cm^2 in females, values approaching those for the buzzard, whose less active and more soaring lifestyle they were converging on (*see* below, under Ecological release and change).

The Marsh Harrier normally kills by pinning its prey to the ground. As it pounces and reaches out to make a strike, the hind talon or talons generally arrive first, penetrating the body of the prey. Falling with its weight onto its prey, or clutching it to it, the harrier's legs double up and the tendons inside pull to tighten the grip. The inner front toe acts in a pincer movement with the hind toe to pierce the prey from both sides. These toes have the longest claws. If the first strike fails to subdue the prey, then a foot can be lifted off and the pincer stabbed in again, several times if necessary (Redhead 1969). Alternatively, the coup de grâce can be delivered with the bill, but not as a matter of course as the falcons do. In the breeding season, prey is generally carried back to the nest secured in one foot, and harriers that come across an opportunity to kill again on their way back have been known to strike with their second foot. If a male then proceeds to drop both prey to a female in a food-pass, this can cause problems!

In relation to its size, the Marsh Harrier generally has larger feet and longer legs than other harriers, allowing it to reach down into long marsh vegetation for prey. The one exception

Harriers pin down or grasp prey in their talons, but may have to kill it finally with their bills.

is leg length in eastern Asia of the Pied Harrier, which proportionately exceeds that of the Eastern Marsh Harrier there and is also thought to be an adaptation for reaching into deep marsh vegetation (Nieboer 1973). The large feet of the Marsh Harrier indicate greater killing capability for its body size. Comparison of the foot size of a male Montagu's Harrier and a female Marsh Harrier demonstrates the range of capabilities within a genus of birds which appear relatively similar in size in the field. This is a clue to their niche separation by size of prey.

The harrier bill reflects no special adaptation. It is again larger in proportion in the Marsh Harrier. This enables it to deal better with the larger prey its larger foot size allows it to catch, and with prey relatively difficult to tear or break open, such as fish, amphibians, reptiles and crustaceans. It also allows it to compete better at carrion. A side view reveals a very pronounced protruding hook to the upper mandible, which is used for tearing food.

Harriers hunt both by sight and by hearing. The forward-facing eyes allow good judgement of distance at the moment of pouncing on prey and major anatomical adaptations have enhanced the directional quality of their hearing, probably making it as important as their eyesight. It is this which determines much of their distinctive lifestyle and makes them harriers. For birds of their size, they have very large ear openings, set in facial discs. The supraorbital ridge forms the effective top to the half-disc, giving the face a fierce expression from some angles. The ridge may also protect the eye from glare, or when attacking prey. The external structure of the facial disc is very specialized. The ruff curves around just behind the ear opening and below the cheek. It is made up of a ridge of skin set densely with stiff perpendicular feathers, curved back with the general lie of the plumage only towards the end of their length. Highly specialized in form, the barbs are very dense and are knitted together by abundant barbules, giving these feathers a silky appearance which reflects light and makes the ruff conspicuous. In the male Marsh Harrier plumage, they are less pigmented and stand out all the more. Lifting the ear-coverts of a Marsh Harrier reveals an oval ear opening approximately 12 mm long and 9 mm wide. The opening begins about 15 mm behind the eye and the forward rim is raised, meaning that sounds tend to enter from behind, by reflection off the ruff of feathers. The ear-coverts lie back flat over a bare cheek and the ear opening, and are also finely adapted, with well-spaced barbs and blunt barbules, with the result that the vane does not knit together as in any normal feather, thereby allowing sound waves to pass through easily whilst still preventing the admission of particles of dirt borne on the wind. The feathers of the various parts of the disc are independently mobile, with their own musculature and nerves, allowing the harrier to direct sound into the ear by lifting feathers and altering the shape of the disc.

So, how exactly are these anatomical features used? In the owls, similar adaptations are for pinpointing prey in darkness, whereas in the harriers they are for pinpointing prey hidden by rank vegetation. The owls differ in that their ear openings are positioned asymmetrically and enable them accurately to gauge the source of a sound not only on the horizontal plane, by turning their head to equalize the amount of noise in each ear, but also on the vertical plane. The lack of asymmetry in the harriers does not drastically cut down their directional hearing ability, however, and it may not be that critical, since in many situations the harrier can use its eyes at the last moment as it appears suddenly over the vegetation, on the correct horizontal course for the prey. An American scientist, William Rice (1982), tested the hearing of the Northern Harrier in laboratory conditions and found that it was almost equal to that of Short-eared and Barn Owls on the horizontal plane. Also working in the laboratory, Van Dijk (in Nieboer 1973) confirmed that the hearing abilities of Montagu's, Hen and Marsh Harriers were better than those of Common Buzzard, Goshawk and Kestrel. The Marsh Harrier therefore has these listening adaptations, but they may be less pronounced than in other harriers and the Marsh Harrier clearly must use them less because it tends to fly higher, giving better vision into tall vegetation but increasing the range for hearing purposes.

It would appear that the harrier's facial discs gather sounds in much the same way as a parabolic reflector. Recent laboratory research on the coding of sound frequency and location in the brain of the Swamp Harrier, however, has found that the upper limit of response is to tones of about 4 kHz (Calford et al. 1985). Calculations of the point at which a facial disc of the size of the harrier's would become directional suggest that this would start only at about 4 kHz, meaning that the disc is too small to have a significant effect on the sound field in the harrier's audible frequency range. Although perhaps too much should not be read into this until it is confirmed by other studies, further research should prove very interesting indeed. The harrier's adaptations with regard to the facial disc and ruff are so similar to those of owls that it is almost inconceivable that they have a different function, but research has already found that the owls' methods of processing sounds in the brain may be quite different.

The sexual dimorphism in plumage of the Marsh Harrier may be significant from a hunting point of view. The much paler underside of the male may give better camouflage against the light sky in the more open situations where he encounters prey. Such camouflage could be less important for the female, as her hunting technique relies more on outright surprise in the more structured habitats in which she prefers to hunt.

Foraging techniques

Marsh Harriers typically fly over likely terrain at 2-6 m above ground level, cold-searching for prey beneath them. The height of flight seems to be linked to the height of the vegetation (Schipper 1977), with taller vegetation requiring higher flight to reduce the angle of vision for the harrier to be able to see down into it. Harriers use a low approach, screened by the vegetation or some other low obstacle. The technique is geared to surprising and closing on prey effectively at the first encounter. Marsh Harriers are not well adapted to give chase; they will go after running prey in the open with some expectation of success, but rarely pursue flying prey. The harriers' typical mode of flight, flapping for a few wingbeats but then gliding may be significant. This produces a rising and falling cadence to their

Research has shown that harriers can pinpoint prey solely from the noise it makes. The stiff ruffs of feathers behind the owl-like facial disks direct sound into large ear openings hidden by flimsy covert feathers.

---

flight, especially in a stiff breeze, and it may be that the glide on still wings assists with stealing up on prey. A typical flight speed for a hunting Marsh Harrier is 20–30 km/hr, but in some circumstances they will hunt more slowly.

The Marsh Harrier shows a greater preference for hunting over tall vegetation such as reedbeds, compared with other harriers. It has a noticeably higher foraging flight and may rely more on visual cues. A varied habitat structure is preferred, with abrupt changes in height of vegetation and other obstacles, giving more opportunities for surprise as they are flown over. Examples are ditches, verges, field edges etc., linear features that are followed by harriers. A harrier may hunt a promising patch of rank vegetation by the more thorough 'quartering' technique, changing direction frequently and flying over the patch several times. It may fly into the wind over part of the habitat, then rising up and quickly gliding back as its wings catch the wind; it then flies back low across the habitat into the wind again while carefully searching for prey concealed in the vegetation. A headwind allows the harrier to remain in control while reducing both its speed, to allow a more thorough search, and its altitude, to allow it to strike more quickly.

The heavier and less agile female Marsh Harrier appears to profit from the greater opportunity for surprise that really tall vegetation such as reeds gives her. Also, as a less manoeuvrable bird, she is not able to react so nimbly to catch prey that she comes upon at very close quarters. Dropping down into reeds that confine prey may give her more latitude, and combined with a slower speed of hunting flight at greater height, reedbed hunting is most typical of the female. Flying into the wind; at times the harrier seems to remain virtually at one spot, clumsily hovering where its interest is aroused. Males are more often seen hunting low and over shorter vegetation. The Marsh Harrier's slower hunting flight, especially that of females, means that it covers less ground than other harriers, but works it more thoroughly. In the breeding season, females hunt mainly on the nesting marsh, but males do tend to range further afield over the other habitats which they are better adapted to exploit.

Often, a Marsh Harrier will test a flock of waterfowl feeding out in the open, leisurely flying at and flushing them, in effect testing for the weak and slow. Hunting for passerine birds requires a fast approach. In Norfolk,

Male hunting over rough grassland. The rank vegetation helps to conceal his approach from potential prey and the light fore-edge to the wing breaks his outline.

flocks of juvenile Starlings feeding out on farmland in late summer are a favourite target. A male Marsh Harrier will fly fast and low towards them, if he is successful seizing one on the ground or in flight (Image 1991). Fast hunting, however, is not commonly used by the Marsh Harrier.

Flying low, harriers often cannot react to prey until they are already passing over it. A 'roll-pounce' as the harrier stalls, spreading its tail and cartwheeling back to dive feet-first at prey is typical; but the strike can also take the form of first hesitating or hovering, and then sideslipping through the air to drop straight down on to the prey, legs outstretched and wings held up. Hesitations in flight/feints occur at some height, but can be quickly checked if the harrier perceives that it has made a mistake or it has no chance of success because the prey has bolted. Stooping at prey and diving to flush it out are rarer, but tactics can become quite cheeky: a Marsh Harrier will occasionally knock a female Pheasant off her feet or even settle on her back, intent on stealing a chick. Harrying of waterfowl such as Coot is common. The waterfowl take to open water at the approach of a harrier and dive if necessary. Defensive behaviour such as grouping, turning on their backs and kicking out has been observed in Coots (Harris 1973). Deliberate holding-down or drowning of smaller waterfowl does occur, Hollands (1984) recounting how one determined Swamp Harrier forced a Coot to dive over and over again until it was exhausted and could be seized. The carcase then has to be retrieved from the water, but it may prove too heavy; in India I have watched Marsh Harriers attempt, unsuccessfully, to lift a waterfowl carcase out of a lake. Hunting prey in the water can also be dangerous, as shown by the drowned Swamp Harrier recovered with its talons embedded in a dead Australian Darter's neck (Vestjens 1972).

It is not generally in harriers' nature to still-hunt in the way that, for example, a Kestrel, Sparrowhawk or Buzzard will – sitting on a vantage point watching for prey and then going for it when it appears. Occasionally, especially where voles are numerous, harriers will 'ground-hunt' – sitting in quite short grass and then leaping on a vole when one appears (Schipper *et al.* 1975). At Minsmere, late one February, King (1961) observed a pair of Marsh Harriers jumping on to tussocks and eating small items in them. On another occasion at Minsmere, Clegg (1961) saw three juveniles attempt ground-hunting, making short bounds with wings flapping, sometimes making a further hop and landing with wings spread, and appearing to miss small items of food. The description of this activity agrees with Cheke's (1987) description of a brood of young Réunion Harriers on the bed of a drying-out lake taking small unidentified items after a 'hop, skip and jump'. Ground-hunting was recorded by Baker-Gabb (1984) as a hunting method of very minor importance for the Swamp Harrier.

The harriers' cold-searching foraging methods and lack of chasing over long distances or stooping make them generally unsuitable for falconry,

To strike, a foraging Marsh Harrier typically spreads its tail to stall, cartwheels over and dives feet-first on prey.

*A harrier
may hesitate
where it detects a
potential prey which
has taken refuge in deep
vegetation, feinting strikes
and choosing the moment to
press one home.*

although the Swamp Harrier has been successfully trained by traditional falconry methods and flown at Rabbits in New Zealand (Wheeldon 1981, 1992). A lot of effort was necessary, though, including selection of harriers which would concentrate on the matter in hand (found to be females 2–3 years old), training harriers to progress from easy young Rabbits to the adults, and flushing or successfully ferreting out Rabbits from their holes. Wheeldon remarked: 'countless hours were spent in the field, but successes were few'.

Strike success rates

Hostile accounts of birds of prey often give the impression that they easily kill everything they go after, well in excess of their food requirements. In actual fact, studies of hunting in a wide range of birds of prey have come up with rather low success rates, typically 5–10 per cent. Rates are difficult to measure for the Marsh Harrier because the dense vegetation in which it hunts can conceal the outcome, although the birds usually soon fly up with prey and carry it at least a short distance to a place where they feel comfortable dealing with it. Schipper (1977), from observation of birds in Holland and France in the breeding season, calculated success rates ranging from 5 to 17 per cent; Underhill-Day (in Clarke in press a) calculated an unusually productive success rate of 27 per cent by six males and one female in the breeding season in East Anglia. Hunting activity is normally reduced or curtailed by rain. This and the effects of wind speed and temperature on success remain to be fully quantified. Schipper (1973) established that rain and stronger winds reduced the rate of prey supplied to the nest.

Kleptoparasitism

Marsh Harriers have stolen a fish from an Osprey (Persson 1971), a Teal from a Peregrine (Williams 1995) and robbed Hen Harriers of prey (Schipper 1977). At Horsey in 1947, Buxton noted a polygynous male Marsh Harrier stealing prey from a widowed female and a pair of Montagu's Harriers; it 'dashed at the hen Montagu and bagging her prey swept off with it in the direction of his own nests'. Baker-Gabb found that Australian Swamp Harriers were dominant in kleptoparasitic encounters, robbing Whistling Kites and a Peregrine Falcon, and repelling the great majority of attacks by Whistling Kites, Little Ravens and a Brown Falcon.

Monitoring food

In the breeding season, the diet of birds of prey is determined from observations of food brought to the nest or by identifying prey remains at plucking places and in pellets. Older studies sometimes relied on the stomach contents of shot birds.

Identification of the prey species by direct observation from a hide is not so easy as might be thought, because the action can be fast. Also, items brought to the nest may not be whole and a good view may not be obtained. Observation from greater distances may allow approximate classification of prey by size alone. The accurate identification of prey remains in harrier pellets requires skills in identifying principally feathers, fur and rodent teeth, but the greatest problem in the breeding season may be in obtaining enough pellets to give a large enough sample. In winter, harrier pellets can be obtained in good quantities from some communal roosts, but tides or winter floods can wash them away and flooded reedbeds can be impossible for a human to search.

Breeding-season diet

The accounts handed down to us by Buxton of food taken in Broadland indicate some specialization by individual harriers, but show that the commonest prey was Moorhen, with leverets and young Pheasants the next most frequent. Young Moorhens, partridges, Pheasants, buntings, a Blackbird, a Starling and a frog were all found over a period at one food cache. In other years, adult Grey Partridges were found at one nest, small Coypus at another, and Moles were noted at a third.

Hosking (1943) made a useful record of the prey brought to a nest at Hickling in 1942, although he regarded it as incomplete since smaller items may have been immediately swallowed whole and gone unrecorded: 71 young birds comprised Pheasants (29), Grey Partridges (21), Red-legged Partridges (8), Meadow Pipits (7), Moorhens (2), Mallard (1), Lapwing (1) and unidentified passerines (2); the mammals comprised Rabbits (15), leverets (7), Field Voles (7), Water Voles (5) and a young rat (1). At Minsmere, Axell (1964) cited Rabbits, very small Coypus, Water Rail and young ducks, Moorhens, Coots, Lapwings, Snipe, partridges and small passerines (Starlings and Yellowhammers).

Recent studies of breeding-season diet in Britain have carried out by Norman Sills and colleagues at Titchwell Marsh, Norfolk, looking at two or three nests each year (Sills 1984), and by John Underhill-Day and volunteers on reclaimed farmland in East Anglia (Underhill-Day 1985). At Titchwell, prey seen to be taken by a male harrier were mainly Starlings one year, owing to the abundance of young Starlings feeding in flocks, and young Pheasants the next, the latter taken in situations where broods had wandered into a field, away from the hedgerow; young Rabbits were also a significant prey. The female took generally larger prey, which she brought to an area of rough, flattened grass for dissection before taking them into the nest. Observers were able regularly to collect remains from the place. A seasonal pattern was noticed with Field Voles taken in May, Moorhens in June

Marsh Harrier pellets from a winter roost on saltmarsh.

and July, and young Rabbits in July. A few partridges, ducklings and passerines, notably Skylark, were taken.

Underhill-Day's study showed a wide variety of prey; adult small passerines and mammals (mostly Field Voles and Rabbits) were predominant in the diet in April–May, but young gamebirds (mostly Pheasants) and waterbirds (mostly ducklings and Moorhens) increased in importance thereafter

In the breeding-season diet elsewhere, Schipper (1973) found that the important categories were young waders and Pheasants, and the larger mammals in Holland, but largely passerines with some waterbirds and larger mammals in northern France, and snakes and larger mammals in southern France. Observations were made of Marsh Harriers eating the eggs of ducks and gulls, but these were not of course visibly represented at the nest. In the Camargue, Thiollay (1970) found the principal foods to be frogs, fish and young waterfowl; eggs, reptiles, small mammals, rats, young Rabbits and, to a lesser extent, small passerines also featured. In Spain, González (1991) found that Rabbits made up 46 per cent of the breeding-season diet, with the rest spread over many categories, none of them approaching Rabbits in importance. Work in Poland, on three pairs of Marsh Harriers nesting at a Coypu farm, showed that the males fed mainly away from nesting marshes on rodents and open-country small passerines, whereas females fed mostly in marshes, on the birds there (Pinowski and Ryszkowski 1961). Predation on young Coypu was found to be negligible, as most hunting took place early in the day whilst Coypus were active in the evening. Witkowski (1989) recorded a significant amount of dead carp (10.5 per cent by number) in the diet at a complex of fishponds in western Poland, Common Vole (14.4 per cent) and Coot (12.4 per cent) among a very wide range of birds (60 per cent), mammals (28 per cent), fish (10 per cent) and frogs (2 per cent); eggs were important early in the season, but could not be quantified. Again, the females hunted the ponds and marshland for large prey and the males concentrated on the meadows and arable fields for smaller prey. In the post-fledging period, as the young of marshland prey species grew up, attention was shifted more to farmland for hunting, especially for voles. In Schleswig-Holstein, Bock (1978) found that the numbers of a wide range of largely small passerine birds taken fell dramatically in a good vole year in favour of the Common Vole. Other prey were negligible in importance, but again a taste for eggs was noted.

Witkowsi (1989) described how the shells of eggs eaten by Marsh Harriers were left with a small hole and claw marks. Egg-eating was actually witnessed by Tom and Pam Gardner (1984) in Australia, where Swamp Harriers were prospecting an ibis colony and a harrier dropped on a temporarily unattended nest, mantling the eggs and scaring neighbouring ibises away. Opening its gape wide, the harrier was able to pick up an egg and drop it on the others to crack it; it then opened it up with its bill and ate the contents. It treated all five eggs similarly and then did the same to a nearby clutch of four eggs, before wiping its bill on the nest and flying off.

These results demonstrate the wide spectrum covered by the breeding-season diet of the Marsh Harrier, tuned to the most profitable prey vulnerableat the particular place and at the time.

Winter diet

Data on winter diet are available from only a very few studies. In one of the most northerly wintering areas, in southern Holland, colleagues and I collected pellets from a roost of up to 30 birds in a reedbed on a large saltmarsh (Clarke *et al.* 1993). In January, February and March, about half the diet by number was ducks. The pellets were packed with feathers and down from Wigeon, Teal, Mallard and a few Pintail, but few contained any lead shot to confirm that these were wounded birds. Moorhens, pigeons and Rabbits were also significant. The rest of the prey comprised a few each of waders, small passerines, rats and various other small mammals. Good samples of winter diet have also been achieved by Thiollay (1970) and Schipper (1973) in the Camargue, where the prey were predominantly wounded ducks, and by Bavoux *et al.* (1990) in Charente-Maritime, France, where mammals made up about 60 per cent of prey – mainly voles, but also significant numbers of Rabbits and Coypus; other prey included a wide variety of birds, but very few ducks. Farther south, in Spain, González found that rats were important in the diet in winter, along with significant numbers of other small mammals, waterfowl and waders.

Marsh Harriers wintering in Africa and India have been seen eating grasshoppers and locusts, but in a far clumsier manner than the smaller Montagu's and Pallid Harriers. On the lagoons at Bharatpur in northern India, the diet was found by Vibhu Prakash to be mainly fish and the smaller waterbirds (mostly Coot, Little Cormorant and Common Teal), with some insects and frogs.

Fishing and carrion-eating

Schipper (1977) observed Marsh Harriers fishing over open water for eels and other fish in the Camargue. Over the sea, Doherty (1978) noted one attempt to join Manx Shearwaters and Black-headed Gulls feeding 400 m from the shore, and King (1978) saw one 'flying very slowly to and fro, quite visibly inspecting the water a metre or so beneath her'. Harriers in Fiji commonly feed on fish, eels and prawns (Clunie 1980). In New Zealand, Stead (1932) regarded wading into water for prey as quite normal for Swamp Harriers; he watched them feeding on tadpoles in small pools on a river-bed, walking into the slimy algae and 'balancing themselves on one foot with the aid of their wings' to catch any tadpoles they may flush.

Carrion-eating was noted in Charente-Maritime (Bavoux *et al.* 1990) and Spain (Gonzalez 1991), and carrion was seen brought to the nest in Holland (Schipper 1973). Goose feathers found in winter pellets from Holland (Clarke *et al.* 1993) almost certainly having come from White-tailed Eagle kills in the area. Carrion features prominently in the diet of the New Zealand Swamp Harrier in some areas, commonly Rabbit, hare and opossum, preferred in that order (Fennell 1980). A preference for smaller carcases that could be carried into cover and for carcases with flesh exposed was found by Robertson (1980), as well as a puzzling preference for baits dyed blue. Preferences may be explained by difficulty experienced in breaking through tough skin. Baker-Gabb (1984) found that there was far more competition for carrion in Australia.

Feeding on insects is occasionally recorded. Marsh Harriers clumsily leap on them in the grass, balancing with outstretched wings.

Consumption and feeding method

How many prey items are taken by nesting Marsh Harriers each season? Underhill-Day (1989) calculated 1118 for an East Anglia pair and their five young up to 1 September. Individual daily food intake has been calculated by few ornithologists. Tollan (1988) carried out food trials with the New Zealand Swamp Harrier in laboratory conditions and the results imply that the amount of fresh weight of food required to maintain the weights of captive harriers were 36 g per day of laboratory mice, 58.6 g of day-old chicks or 42.9 g of fish. This compares with a figure of 120 g found to be the full crop weight in the captive New Zealand Harrier by Fox (1977a), 76.5 g of food estimated by Gonzalez (1991) for wild Marsh Harriers in Spain, and 50–100 g estimated for adults by Thiollay (1970) in the Camargue.

The Marsh Harrier is more inclined to feed on carrion than other harrier species are. Its larger size enables it to compete on more even terms with other scavengers.

Food is held down with a foot. A harrier will stand on larger carcases, plucking feathers from avian prey or stripping off the skin of larger mammals, and then tearing off pieces of meat with a pull and twist of the bill. The tail is pressed down, and sometimes also the wings, for balance, as the harrier pulls at the carcase. The description by Brichambaut (1978) of how a Marsh Harrier began to tackle a Muskrat is valuable. The harrier was disturbed from the kill at a stage when the skin had been detached from the head at the neck and very cleanly drawn back over the body towards the tail; the head remained intact with the skin on, while the forelegs were nothing more than bones (still attached) stripped of flesh.

Sympatry and generalist/specialist food niches

Potentially, harriers living in sympatry are in conflict over food resources. When winter Marsh Harrier pellets from Holland were compared with pellets from an adjacent Hen Harrier roost (Clarke *et al.* 1993) we found that, although the Hen Harriers were eating ducks, they were playing a more general predator role with a wider food niche. They caught high numbers of small passerines in November, but concentrated on small mammals in December and January, and on lagomorphs in February and even more so in March. The Marsh Harrier diet of predominantly ducks remained constant, and in this way there was not a great conflict over prey resources. It seems that the smaller Hen Harrier may have a lower threshold of cost/benefit before it can switch to an alternative prey where hunting effort is rewarded by adequate prey biomass.

The contents of one winter pellet – bill tip and head feathers from a male Wigeon.

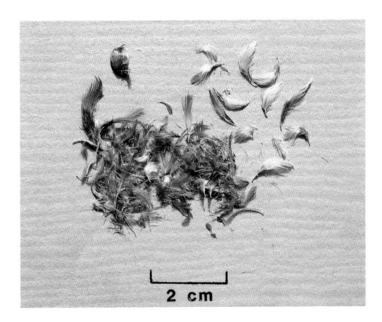

2 cm

Vole highs have specialization on them by foraging Marsh Harriers (e.g., Bakker 1946, Bock 1978). The Marsh Harrier's larger body size and clumsier pouncing may mean that relatively small prey such as voles have to be very abundant before the energy spent catching them is balanced by the nutritional reward.

Ecological release and change

The isolation of harrier populations in island environments has had measurable modifying effects on their morphological and behavioural characteristics related to foraging. These reveal much about the plasticity of the niche of Marsh Harriers in relation to competition and different environments.

The Swamp Harrier in New Zealand has little competition, since the only other resident diurnal raptor is the New Zealand Falcon, which is similar to the Peregrine and does not forage for carrion. Free of competition from the usual range of carrion-feeding buzzards, kites and eagles, the harrier often forages over farmland habitats with short grass and has taken to frequent soaring when foraging, and feeding on sheep carrion and road kills, sometimes becoming an incidental road casualty itself as a result. The dietary and behavioural differences between the New Zealand and the Australian Swamp Harriers, the latter being more 'normal' members of the Marsh Harrier complex, have been measured (Baker-Gabb 1986). It is interesting to compare them, as follows.

Australia	New Zealand
Competition for carrion from Little Ravens, Brown Falcons, Whistling Kites and Brown Goshawks	Competition for carrion only from Kelp Gulls
Low hunting flight when over rank vegetation or open water	Ditto
No high prospecting flight and almost no soaring	Much soaring over open farmland with short grass, and flying high transects along rows of trees and roads
Approaches baits from low flight	Planes or spirals down to bait from a height
Significantly fewer dive attacks	
Rabbits eaten were not in short grass	Rabbits eaten all in open farmland with short grass
Sheep rare in diet (but common in area)	Sheep common in diet
Annual diet 62 per cent birds	Annual diet 71 per cent mammals
House mice and waterfowl significant in autumn and winter diet (sheep and road kills)	Mammalian carrion significant in autumn and winter diet
Significantly longer tarsi*	Significantly shorter tarsi*
Rarely nests away from wetlands	Uses a wide range of dry habitats for nesting

*(Long tarsi are assumed to be an adaptation to hunting in long vegetation)

Fox (1977a) noted that the New Zealand Swamp Harrier was not yet adopting the higher perches, such as telegraph poles, typical of buzzards. He also found an interesting phenomenon, illustrative of the problems encountered by a population in the early stages of adaptation. On two individuals examined, a length of tough tissue from carrion had wrapped itself around the base of the arrow-shaped, behind the backward-pointing tips. The shape of the tongue is useful for clearing food from the upper palate, but long tissue wrapped around it caused swelling and infection and was likely to be fatal in untreated wild birds.

The period of isolation of the New Zealand Harrier is estimated at about 10,000 years from fossil records, but it is probably not complete since migrants from Australia may be blown there off course in the prevailing westerly winds. Furthermore, a drastic transformation of the landscape from mainly forest to sheep-grazing pasture dates from European settlement. Behavioural and morphological differences may therefore be relatively recent. The activities of acclimatization societies led to the introduction of Rabbits and other European fauna. The Rabbit was the principal food and, although its population was brought under control by myxomatosis and poisoning in the 1950s, Rabbits, mainly young ones, still remain the main food in some areas, and even after their rotational control by poisoning (Pierce and Maloney 1989). Farther west, the Polynesian harrier is described as less of a scavenger than the New Zealand bird and has been seen hunting through forest (Brown and Child 1975) and fishing by swooping low over the water and raking with the feet (Clunie 1980), although there are only two other diurnal raptors in competition with it.

The Réunion and Madagascar Harriers are more profoundly isolated, being located off the east coast of Africa as well distant from their presumed ancestor (*spilonotus*) in eastern Asia. Réunion is a small volcanic island of very rugged terrain and mostly >1000 m above sea level, very unpromising habitat for harriers. Surprisingly, the Réunion Harrier is found mostly in forest, which until recent times covered the whole island. It hunts over or between the trees in the harrier manner, taking prey from the canopy or the ground. It is the only raptor on the island (although a type of kestrel there is now extinct) and its niche appears to have expanded into very unfamiliar territory for a harrier. Before the introduction of foreign species, the only mammals were bats, and the Réunion Harrier's prey would have been made up very largely of pigeons, parrots and other birds. It has developed particularly extreme morphological characteristics which all substantiate adaptation to these circumstances. Compared with other harriers, the wings are broad, short and blunt at the tip, as found in forest-dwelling hawks such as the Sparrowhawk; the tarsus is relatively short (an adaptation corresponding with larger prey in the hawks), the claws and middle toe are longer, and the RSD – reversed size dimorphism – is more marked (all corresponding with predominantly avian prey in the hawks) (Clouet 1978).

11

MOULT AND BIOMETRICS

The moulting strategy of the Marsh Harrier is built around the breeding cycle, and possibly migration, too. The female begins to moult in April/May with the onset of egg-laying, and the male begins about a month later. Both generally complete their moults in about October. Sizes of some feathers critical to flight and moult timing appear to develop in tune with the maturation of the birds. The study of moult is necessarily based on captive birds, which may be affected hormonally by various factors. Nevertheless, some useful facts have been established.

The moult of primary feathers is complete each year. In a captive male over a period of seven years, Zuppke (1987) found that primary moult generally began in late May or early June and was strictly in descendent order, from the inner first primary to the outer tenth, with the last primary finally shed at dates varying from mid September to early January. As each feather dropped out, the replacement took on average 25 days to grow fully. Interestingly, the corresponding outer primaries 7 to 10 collected each year showed a significant increase in length over the first two or three moults, so that wing length increased as the bird matured. The duration of the moult varied from 137 to 224 days, from shedding the first feather to shedding the last. Moult in the male is thought to occur at a slower rate, and this may be to enable him to hunt efficiently at a critical period. The interval between feathers in Zuppke's male gradually lengthened on average through the moult, the first few feathers being shed at a stage when the demands of young in the nest would be less. In females, the moult is much more rapid for the first four or five feathers and occurs during incubation and brooding, resulting in larger gaps in the wing at a time when flight is less important; these gaps can easily be seen in flight when the female leaves the nest at this stage.

The BTO Guide on moult (1983) states that secondary moult begins from three points, or centres: at first and fifth secondaries (numbered from outermost inwards)in ascendant (inwards) order and from the innermost, thirteenth secondary in descendent order. In his captive male, Zuppke confirmed that secondary moult started from three centres but found that it was not complete each year, and a descending or ascending order could not be established from the centres. The complex strategy may ensure that no significant gaps form and may be synchronized with migration in some way. The fourth, seventh, eighth and ninth secondaries were retained for two years beginning from the second moult. The inner and outer secondary feathers also increased in length over the first two or three moults, altering the shape of the wing. The alula feathers were moulted in descendent order over the period from July to October and increased in length. Tail moult occurred over a period from June to September and always in the same order: (of six feathers on each side, numbered from the centre of the tail) left 1, 6, 3, 4, 2, 5 and right 1, 3, 6, 4, 2, 5: feathers 3 and 6 were not, therefore, shed as a pair.

The post-juvenile moult begins in the first winter with head and body feathers, and sometimes some tail feathers, but the flight and tail feathers may be replaced in the second calendar-year to a faster timetable than that of adults. Zuppke found that shedding of all the primaries took 137, 220 and 224 days in calendar-years two, three and four respectively, but then decreased again to 138 days by year eight. Altenburg et al. (1987) noticed that non-breeding Marsh Harriers in immature plumage began to moult earlier than breeders.

Biometrics

The first study to take a really large sample of measurements of Marsh Harriers in Europe was by Bavoux et al. (1988). The mean body weights of those of known sex were 633 g for males (range 530–730 g) and 836 g for females (range 720–960 g), showing a small overlap. In the absence of other clear characteristics, sex could therefore be predicted best (93 per cent success) by body weight. Bill length, tarsus length and tarsus width were found to be less reliable. By combining body weight and bill length in a discriminant formula, success was increased significantly, to 99.1 per cent.

12

LIFESPAN AND MORTALITY

The potential lifespan of raptors tends to increase with size of the species. As medium-sized raptors, harriers have maximum recorded lifespans in the range of 16–18 years. Examples of record longevity in wild Marsh Harriers include a bird from the northern Netherlands of 16 years and 220 days (Bijlsma 1993) and one from Czechoslovakia in its nineteenth year (Ilyichew 1982). One Swamp Harrier reached 18 years and 2 months (Henny in Newton 1990).

Any study of lifespan and mortality in the wild requires the marking of birds. The existing records of length of life are based on ringing recoveries. These give some idea of the pattern of mortality, but take a very long time to provide any quantity of data and may be subject to bias due to ring loss and the quirks of reporting.

Harriers are typical of birds of prey in that the highest mortality is in the first year, when most deaths occur through starvation or accidents through inexperience. Of 34 recoveries of birds ringed in the Camargue, 22 (65 per cent) were less than one year old, five were 1–2 years old, four 2–3 years, two 3–4 years and one 11 years (Thiollay 1970). A review of 17 Marsh Harriers ringed in the northern Netherlands (Bijlsma 1993) showed that mean life expectancy for birds recovered after one year was about 4.9 years; it began to tail off sharply after the age of about 12. Bijlsma commented that Dijkstra found a much lower figure going back over all recoveries of Dutch birds. After about 1970, increased survival seems to bear out the effects of increased protection and the bans on organochlorine pesticides. Of 358 individuals ringed in Czechoslovakia, East Germany, Poland and the former USSR (Ilyichew 1982), 46 per cent of those recovered died in their first year, after which the mean life expectancy was about three years, with only two attaining ages of more than 12; at least 44 per cent were killed by man.

Nests can fail from any one of a range of causes, including predation, flooding, desertion, egg breakage, eggs not hatching, and mortality of the young. The greatest mortality in young nestlings is from chilling in prolonged periods of rain and cold. In Britain, nest failures due to desertion and egg-collecting were the largest categories from 1911 to 1982 (Underhill-Day 1984); in the subsequent ten years, 15 per cent of nests failed in Britain (Underhill-Day in Gibbons et al. 1993).

Crows, Foxes and Mink were implicated in predation of eggs or young in Sweden (Bengtson 1967), Wild Boar, Stoats, Polecats, martens and White-tailed Eagle in Poland (Witkowski 1989), and crows, Stoats, Foxes and Bitterns in Britain (Underhill-Day 1984). The Fox is potentially the most important predator of Marsh Harrier nests in Britain, especially as breeding occurs increasingly in dry crops. The omnivorous Bittern, a very natural reedswamp neighbour of the Marsh Harrier, is quite capable in defence against harrier mobbing and can nest in close proximity. Its fledging young forage in the reedbed. Bert Axell drew attention to this factor. Writing in 1977, he stated that at least six desertions of their nests by harriers at Minsmere could be attributed to Bitterns: 'Caught in the act of raiding a nest, a Bittern stands with its awesome three-inch beak pointing upwards, and the harrier, which tries to defend its nest only by swooping at its enemy, lifts its talons clear just in time at the bottom of each dive'. This seemed to be an important factor, with up to 14 pairs of Bitterns (a count now known to be too high because booming males move around) and only up to four of Marsh Harriers there. Sills (1983) noted that Bittern-mobbing was an important activity in the last two-thirds of the nestling stage at Titchwell; it was provoked if a Bittern approached within 80 m of the nest, and intensified if it got closer, but no losses to Bitterns were actually recorded there.

Surprisingly, Witkowski (1989) found that crows were no problem and that most eggs were eaten by the harriers themselves. He noticed that incubating females damaged the most eggs as they frequently shifted position when it was raining. When organochlorines were in widespread use, thin-shelled eggs were more likely to sustain accidental damage and eventually be eaten because they were imperfect. Witkowski also noted adaptation in the siting of nests in response to predation by Wild Boar, with a significant shift towards the water's edge and hence to reeds in deeper water. The possibility of terrestrial predators following human tracks to nests must be considered by any researcher.

Mortality in the nest is linked to sex and also to mating status of the parents. Altenburg et al (1982) found that malnutrition was an important cause of mortality in the nest. Young that died later were consistently below average weight. Male nestlings of secondary females in polygynous relationships had a lower-than-average body weight, and it seemed that they were the first to suffer because female young were larger. Many polygnous females are forced to hunt at an earlier stage, and there is an inherently greater risk of chilling of eggs and mortality of young nestlings, since they will not enjoy as much brooding as at nests of monogamous females.

13

THREATS AND CONSERVATION

The Marsh Harrier would seem to be much more vulnerable than many raptors. Virtually restricted to one threatened habitat, and sensitive to disturbance, the status of its breeding populations in western Europe is largely dependent on conditions farther south. It is mainly a migrant to or through southern Europe, where its relatively low and slow flight has made it a prime target for the largely outdated shooting woven into the fabric of parts of society there. However, the international community, either on a voluntary basis through appeals such as at the British Birdwatching Fair or through legislation such as EU Directives, is increasingly taking action to counter problems to wildlife. Also on the plus side, the Marsh Harrier can be a relatively prolific breeder and is suitably wary of man. Given a measure of protection from persecution and environmental contaminants, Marsh Harrier numbers have responded well.

The relatively strong standing of the Marsh Harrier today contrasts with the much weaker position of Montagu's Harrier over much of Europe. The Montagu's more fragile ecology, based on long-distance migration by the

Thousands of Marsh Harriers run the gauntlet of illegal shooting around the Mediterranean. Raptors migrating slowly and low over the water after a long sea crossing are vulnerable to being pursued and shot from boats.

whole population, smaller prey and the use of a variety of habitats that are threatened or unsuitable, is probably the reason. However, I was struck by the incongruity of the European situation recently as I watched both species nesting side by side in thick marshes in western Asia. Montagu's Harrier was by far the predominant species there, yet it seems to abandon nesting in marshes in western Europe in favour of crops and other dry habitats where it may be so much more vulnerable, thankfully a trend less evident in the Marsh Harrier.

Because the numbers of Marsh Harriers were so depressed for so long in Britain, we have probably had a mistaken conception of the species' potential. Numbers have begun to increase much faster in very recent years, and it has become difficult to keep track of all nesting birds in quite the same intimate way we have. The distribution of the species in Britain is still very local, however, and it has a long way to go before we can say that it is really secure; in Britain the Marsh Harrier is very definitely a Red Data Book bird, although in Europe as a whole it is not a critically threatened species. It was widely believed that the British population would ultimately be severely limited by the availability of *large* reedbeds, but this is proving not to be the case, with pairs breeding in little more than ditches in favourable areas. Semi-colonial use of suitable nesting habitat enables the species to maximize use of reedbeds.

It should be possible to encourage, anticipate and predict range expansion for the Marsh Harrier and actively to promote its return to many of the counties in Britain that lost the species in the nineteenth century. The key to this must be in the restoration of a network of undisturbed wetlands. It seems that sites need not necessarily be large, but should be created in areas with riverine and other suitable hunting habitat which can be exploited by the species once it has a safe reedbed nesting site. Breeding Marsh Harriers are rather sensitive to human access at small sites and so in new areas they should initially be encouraged to establish themselves on secluded private land, although the 'honeypot' principle of attracting birdwatchers to just a few large sites to see the species will provide valuable publicity and public support. The ultimate potential population for the species in modern Britain could conceivably be a few hundred nests.

Habitat conservation and creation

In Britain, the loss of reedbed habitat has been halted, although the preservation of marshes goes beyond their boundaries into the catchment area, where water abstraction and lowering of the water table is a threat to their existence. The surviving large reedbeds are now largely secure in nature reserves, bar the threat of overriding commercial interests (which are allowed the upper hand by force of government veto in large development and road schemes at some key locations). At the time of writing, the strength of enforcement of the EU Directive on habitats has yet to be proved.

Enormous changes have occurred on the margins bordering the large reedbeds where Marsh Harriers nest. The ultra-intensive arable farming of recent

ABOVE *Eastern Marsh Harrier (insert – male Pied) (Japan)*
CENTRE *African Marsh Harrier* BELOW *Swamp Harrier (Australia)*

107

decades has left the harriers hunting more at field edges and over crops rather than over the rough grazing or wasteland that used to abut reedbeds. This does not appear to have been detrimental and may have been beneficial, since the harriers prefer to hunt the young partridges, Pheasants and Starlings common in arable countryside as much as the now rarer birds and mammals of grazing marshes. In fact, grazing marshes in use were probably not structured to the Marsh Harrier's advantage, being low-growing and enabling prey to keep an eye on the progress of the predator. The Marsh Harrier is becoming closely associated with agricultural land in eastern England. At Titchwell, the importance of use of farm tracks, verges, patches of scrub and young plantations was noted (Sills 1988). Underhill-Day (in Clarke in press b) stressed the importance of watercourses, in his area ditches and a small river.

In the east of England, especially the low-lying rich fenland of Lincolnshire, Cambridgeshire and Norfolk, and as some farming land is taken out of production in the permanent set-aside scheme, there would appear to be a lot of scope for the creation of small wetlands as viable Marsh Harrier nesting sites if the regulations allow them under the scheme. The embankment of large artificial wetlands can be expensive, but there are many corners by rivers or drains that could be enlarged into small reedbeds and the water level maintained by modern methods. Overmanagement of bankside vegetation on many waterways, ostensibly to maintain the speed of flow, is of great detriment to wildlife such as the Marsh Harrier. Reedbed ronds alongside rivers both prevent bank erosion from boat and tidal wash and are potential nest sites in undisturbed reaches. Rotational commercial cutting of reed could be used to defray some of the costs of larger schemes. Expensive schemes for the restoration of wetlands to the fens could be undertaken hand in hand with sporting interests, to the benefit of all. All too widely in Britain there has been a distinct divide between sporting and conservation lobbies, and the lack of the ecomomic muscle of such cooperative schemes has often held back progress for rare species. The presence of Marsh Harriers indicates that the game population is healthy, and wherever fenland drains criss-cross the landscape a supply of suitable waterfowl such as Moorhen, Coot and Mallard could be encouraged with appropriate management. Pheasants originate from swampy habitats in China and thrive in reedbeds. The restoration of worked-out mineral excavations such as gravel pits also offers many opportunities to create reedbed habitat. The participation of water authorities can provide some important opportunities. Reedbeds also provide a natural form of effluent purification and could be more widely used in that role on the coast and alongside rivers, where the addition of reed to other suitable habitat could produce a very suitable environment overall for Marsh Harriers.

The main practical considerations in creating a large new reedbed ideally include the establishment of separate compartments with independent water-level control, variation in water depth to give the diverse structure of most benefit to a wide range of wildlife and allow some access, and the availability of resources for continuing management. However, the establishment of smaller stands with more rudimentary management can still be of great benefit, especially linear reedbeds or ronds on the edge of the deeper waterways and longer-lived reedbeds on the coast, where salinity prevents colonization by other plants and tidal action slows the build-up of sediment.

For so many species of raptor in Britain, conservation means the retention of large tracts of natural or semi-natural habitat in the north and west. In contrast, here is an opportunity to do something in the less remote regions of Britain and hand in hand with modern industry and farming.

Habitat management

Active management of reedbeds is of paramount importance. The aim should be to maintain a very wet reedswamp and hold the succession process towards woodland. The majority of Marsh Harrier nests are among vegetation standing in water. In an unmanaged reedbed, the leaf litter dropping annually from reed gradually reduces the depth of water. Other plants can then take hold, eventually including shrubs such as willow growing up into carr or damp woodland which is difficult and costly to remove once it takes hold. Reed-cutting, raking and burning slow the accumulation of litter, but have to be carefully planned on a rotational basis to maintain a diverse structure to the reedbed as a whole. Annual cutting gives the best-quality reed in the short term, but blanket annual cutting is totally unsuitable for nesting Marsh Harriers and many other marsh birds such as Reed Warbler, Bearded Tit, Bittern and Water Rail, since it leaves no growth in early spring to conceal their nests. Others, such as Snipe and Garganey, prefer cut reed. Reed will tolerate seasonal drops in water level below the soil surface, but it grows best in levels that do not fluctuate irregularly. The ability to control water levels is therefore desirable, especially since it will enable reedcutters to get on to the site when they need to.

It is normally desirable to drain a commercial reedbed for the winter, since reed left standing in water for too long can suffer from unsightly blacking at the base or can remain green below the waterline and therefore vulnerable to mould and decay when cut and bundled. Winter draining is not a problem for Marsh Harriers. Cutting every two years (known as 'double wale') produces a greater quantity of reed than annual cutting, and although some of the older stems have to be discarded it may in some circumstances be more economic from a commercial point of view and allow Marsh Harriers to nest in the year-old reed. The commercial value of the output, however, has to be carefully considered. Reed undergoes colour changes with age and weathering, causing problems with its aesthetics in thatching. Yellow in their first winter, stems two years old can look pinkish and at three years silvery. A mix of ages can produce irregular patterns on the thatched roof. Substantial stands of reed should be left for longer than the rotational cutting cycle, to encourage insects and the other reedbed fauna dependent on the build-up of old material. Marsh Harriers can use these older stands, too. Reed may have to be protected from large Starling roosts, which can flatten wide areas, and in some circumstances from grazing stock, since they find reed shoots very succulent. The maintenance of open water is important, to maintain the population of wildfowl and to provide the diverse structure and especially the habitat edge used by hunting Marsh Harriers. Reed 'hover' will tend to grow out horizontally over undisturbed deep water without rooting and may need to be cut free and removed. In due course, areas of the reedbed that are drying out may need to be excavated and opened up to water again.

Access management

Although nest sites in reedswamp can be protected from human access relatively easily, the effect of open access to surrounding habitat is to reduce the usable hunting ranges for the harriers. This can be particularly detrimental if the areas affected contain optimum foraging habitat, and also later in the breeding season, when tourism increases at the same time as the food requirements of Marsh Harrier young reach their peak. In a study on the Neusiedler See in eastern Austria, which has one of the most important Marsh Harrier populations in central Europe, the harriers would fly no closer to visible tourist activity than an estimated 90 m in the open; routes frequently used by cyclists and walkers created a no-go corridor for Marsh Harriers 240 m wide, severely limiting the prime foraging habitat available to them (Gamauf 1993). Appropriate screening of paths and other areas of open access is therefore of paramount importance in reserve design. At Titchwell Marsh, a very heavily visited RSPB reserve in Norfolk with unscreened paths alongside the freshwater and tidal reedbeds, Sills (1983) found that Marsh Harriers would not build closer than 450 m to a path and on average sited their nests 600 m from the footpath to the west and 800 m from that to the east; this was in response to a regular and at times constant flow of people. Because of the proximity of so many nest sites to sea walls, the Marsh Harrier may be vulnerable to disturbance from leisure developments such as long-distance coastal footpaths.

Protection schemes

Although undoubtedly responsible for the total extinction of the species as a British breeding bird at the turn of the century, persecution is currently not a big problem for the Marsh Harrier in Britain, but it could become more of a limiting factor as numbers increase. In the ten years up to 1988, 22 incidents of persecution were recorded (Underhill-Day in Gibbons et al. 1993); most individuals were shot, trapped or were the victims of the indiscriminate use of poisoned baits. Two recovered at Snettisham in north Norfolk in 1985 were suffering from gunshot wounds. The species is prone to the illegal and careless use of poison, since it comes readily to both carrion and eggs, which are the principal vehicles used for poisoned baits. The setting of unprotected poison baits in the open is illegal in the UK. In 1980, the male of the first pair to attempt nesting in Scotland for many years was found poisoned (Buckland et al. 1990). Unrecorded persecution in the form of intentional disturbance of birds interested in breeding may be a problem in some areas.

Game interests are concerned with the impact of raptor predation on lowland gamebirds, which do form a proportion of the food of the Marsh Harrier. Calculations based on brood-size counts of Mallard, Pheasant and partridges in one study by Underhill-Day (1989) indicated that many of the chicks taken by Marsh Harriers would have died before reaching maturity. The number fledged was reduced by about 13 per cent for Mallard and 11 per cent for Pheasant. He recorded very few partridge chicks taken, perhaps because they stay closer to cover at field edges than Pheasants do. Delaying release until Pheasant poults are of a good size and the peak food demands of breeding Marsh Harriers

The interface of leisure activities and harrier breeding habitat requires careful management. Marsh Harriers are notoriously prone to deserting their nests.

are well past would be a good management strategy; effective cover for poults would also reduce predation. Calculating the losses of gamebirds to raptor predation entails a great deal of work in recording the large number of variables: food delivery rates in each phase of the breeding cycle, diet composition, hunting-range size, gamebird density, and brood sizes of both predator and prey.

Any prejudice against raptors cannot effectively be met by enforcement of the law alone. The requirements of the species in the modern landscape must be frankly discussed between landowners and ornithologists on the basis of sound scientific data and an acceptable position be reached by means of manipulation of the habitat.

In recent years, about half the British Marsh Harrier population has bred in nature reserves or under some form of wardening scheme. The RSPB has wardened a number of vulnerable sites off nature reserves, especially in west Norfolk (where a few pairs of Montagu's Harriers also breed), and in Somerset, for example, the Hawk and Owl Trust has combined with the county Wildlife Trust to warden Marsh Harriers. Routine farming operations are a threat to crop-nesting harriers, making it necessary to keep track of locations of nests and to liaise with the farms involved. Spraying during incubation appears to cause no harm if the nest is avoided by the tractor wheels! Later, the young have to be temporarily covered or removed or the spray turned off as the boom passes over the vicinity of the nest. Spray drift also has to be considered. Crops often grow unnaturally thick and can smother the nest and young, especially in wet weather; oilseed rape is a particular danger in this respect. The crop may have to be cut back at the nest to give the young a better chance.

The time of greatest danger is at harvest. Marsh Harriers nest earlier than Montagu's, and tend to have fledged by harvest time, but where they have not action has to be taken to protect nest from combining operations. It may be possible to agree a delay in harvesting until the young fledge. Otherwise the young should be temporarily removed in a ventilated cardboard box during

Crop-nesting is becoming more prevalent in some regions of Britain and farmers there are becoming more aware. Routine farming operations need to be planned carefully to avoid harming the eggs or young.

combining. The advice used to be to leave a small patch of the crop containing the nest. Alternatively, the young could be permanently removed to a new site, on the field edge for example, where the adults could find them, or be replaced at the original site protected by a wall of bales. Where the nest is in wheat or barley, rather than oilseed rape, a recent innovation promoted in both ornithological and farming journals by the RSPB, known as the 'total harvest' method, should be used. The header on the harvester is raised so that only the ears are cropped, and the stubble is left long over an area the width of the harvester's cut and ideally for a distance of 12–15 m. The nest site thereby remains less conspicuous. Such practical conservation work with a Schedule 1 species at the nest requires a licence from English Nature or the appropriate local agency.

Farther south, in France and Spain, the campaign to protect nests in crops has become a highly organized affair, with the French bird-of-prey protection organization Fonds d'Intervention pour les Rapaces (FIR) the leader in this field. Statistics published by FIR since 1982 show an increase in the number of Marsh Harriers nesting in crops, but the proportion is very low compared with the numbers of Montagu's or even Hen Harriers using them.

The occasional clutch has been lost to egg-collectors, but although significant and deplorable this does not appear to be a serious problem for the Marsh Harrier. Of 92 failed nests in Britain, at least 17.4 per cent were due to egg-collectors (Underhill-Day 1984).

Pesticides

In the 1950s and 1960s, the organochlorine insecticides, DDT and the cyclodienes aldrin, dieldrin, endrin and heptachlor, were used widely in agriculture and forestry. As a side effect, these compounds dissolved in fat and accumulated in predators, particularly those eating birds feeding on arable fields. In the strongly arable east of England, they were used as seed dressings to counter soil pests such as wheat-bulb fly and carrot fly. Apart from direct mortality, the effects on raptors were to cause embryo death and eggshell thinning leading to a high rate of breakages. A further group of organochlorines known as the PCBs, compounds used as plasticizers in industry, also causes embryo deaths. Severe population declines became apparent in the Sparrowhawk and Peregrine in Britain. The Kestrel population was also reduced, but less markedly, perhaps because of its mainly mammal diet. At the same time, both Montagu's and Marsh harriers declined sharply, but, because of their very low numbers in Britain and observers' unawareness, concrete evidence was not available conclusively to implicate the organochlorines. For example, infertile eggs were increasingly noted in nests in Poole Harbour, Dorset, from 1956 and others were retrospectively suspected of having been removed by the birds, but 'observers assumed that unhatched eggs were infertile due to natural causes and it therefore never occurred to them to have eggs analysed' (Chapman 1977). Numbers of Marsh Harriers dropped from about 15 pairs to one and those of Montagu's from about thirty pairs to none, both over the critical period from the late 1950s to the early 1970s.

A large number of bird-of-prey deaths reported in the Netherlands in the 1968/69 winter coincided with the sowing of winter cereals dressed with organochlorines. A Marsh Harrier was among the birds obtained for analysis. The bird was found dying in convulsions from diadrin poisoning and had a level of 28 parts per million (ppm) in its liver, compared with a lethal threshold of about 15–20 ppm (Koeman *et al.* 1969).

Eggshell thinning was measured in several studies. Underhill-Day (1984) found a decrease in shell thickness of 10 per cent when comparing British Marsh Harrier eggs before 1945 with those in the period 1948 to 1981. This does not appear to have been severe enough to affect hatching success, since brood size per nest did not fall. In Poland, Witkowski (1989) found that

In autumn, juvenile Marsh Harriers will attempt to roost in the very last of the cereal crop.

eggs laid in the years 1972–75 were 23 per cent thinner-shelled than pre-1945 European eggs. Losses due to breakage were high. Full testing for organochlorines was carried out on unhatched Marsh Harrier eggs collected from nests in central Sweden in the period 1968 to 1976 (Odsjo and Sondell 1977). The levels of pesticides and PCBs in 113 eggs were correlated with breeding success at the nests from which the eggs were taken. Shell thickness was shown to be on average 14 per cent less after 1946. Samples from the tips of tail feathers of nestlings analysed for mercury showed higher levels in nests before the ban in 1966 in Sweden on the use of methyl mercury as a seed-dressing agent, which was far more lethal than the ethyl-mercury used in Britain. Odsjo and Sondell detected a decrease in average number of young per pair, from 3.72 in 1919–49 to 3.03 in 1966–76. This appeared to be offset by the decreased persecution in western Europe, and the population was rising in spite of the effects of organochlorines and heavy metals.

In Britain, bans on organochlorines came in in stages for various applications. Their withdrawal as seed dressings for spring-sown cereals took place in 1962 and for autumn-sown in 1975. The distribution of PCBs for their most dispersive uses ceased in the early 1970s. The recovery of the Marsh Harrier population, beginning in 1972, coincided with the withdrawal of organochlorines and PCBs, further circumstantial evidence of their terrible effect. There is clearly a need to monitor the contamination level by regular analysis of, corpses and unhatched eggs. In Britain, such work is carried out by the Institute of Terrestrial Ecology, where a national database is kept on the results of analysis of corpses and eggs of predatory birds.

Lead poisoning

The issue of lead poisoning has been very much to the fore in recent years. Perhaps the most notorious example of lead poisoning among raptors involved the California Condor, where the tiny relict population probably suffered for years from ingesting lead bullets in unrecovered game. The accumulation of lead in smaller raptors may not be so acute, since they regurgitate the shot quite quickly in their pellets, but those such as the Marsh Harrier that frequently take advantage of dead and moribund gamebirds and mammals in regions where shooting pressure is high may be exposed to significant accumulation of lead over the period when the indigestible elements taken in with food are retained in the acid of the upper stomach. Pain et al. (1993) found that Marsh Harriers trapped in France had much higher levels of lead in their blood than the generally accepted background level: up to 17.5 per cent of pellets they collected from roosts in Charente-Maritime contained shot, which appeared to be from shot Rabbits or Coypu. This is a far higher proportion than the three pellets containing shot out of 109 my collegues and I collected in Holland in the shooting season and which contained largely the remains of wildfowl (Clarke et al. 1993), showing that the problem is probably concentrated in certain regions. The worst areas for such poisoning are likely to be in the southern European wetlands, where many Marsh Harriers winter and shooting pressure is very high. Technically feasible alternative to lead shot urgently need to be developed and sold.

The problem of shooting in southern Europe

The Marsh Harrier is one of the species seriously affected by the the intense pressure of shooting in the Mediterranean countries at migration times. In his brave book *Fatal Flight* (1992), Natalino Fenech catalogues the obsession in his native Malta with the killing of birds. The Marsh Harrier figures very significantly in the sad statistics. Malta lies south of Sicily as a stepping stone on the central migratory route across the Mediterranean, and large numbers of harriers have been shot each spring and autumn, both from land and from sea-craft. Making a long sea crossing, birds of prey fly low because of the absence of thermals. They can be spotted from a distance and pursued in fast rubber craft with outboard motors. Of an estimated 50,000–80,000 birds of prey shot as they ran the gauntlet of Malta each year, 10,000 were reckoned to be Marsh Harriers. There is debate about the numbers, but clearly the have been high. These are birds shot for 'sport' and taxidermy. This practice will continue while the laws that are made are not enforced, and the issue remains a political football to curry favour with the hunting lobby in the two-party politics of the island. Malta

This male was destined for a life in an aviary after badly breaking his wing by colliding with power lines soon after fledging. At two years old, his sub-adult plumage shows traces of barring on the wings reminiscent of the ringtail plumage in other harrier species. The barring on the wing, outer tail feathers and rum disappears with age

has now signed the Berne Convention and will be faced with the EU Directive if it joins the EU, but the problem of enforcement is perhaps the greatest hurdle. Open disregard for the licensing laws makes bureaucratic control impossible. Malta has not been the only black hole for the birds which others treasure and nurture farther north. Other Mediterranean islands have suffered similar adverse publicity, as have parts of mainland southern Europe and north Africa. Protection laws for all birds of prey were enacted in Italy in 1977, but thousands of poachers have caused problems by pursuing their outmoded practices; organizations such as MOS and LIPU deserve our fullest possible backing. The problem has been getting the publicity it deserves, and political pressure is at last beginning to be felt in some quarters.

Collision

Harriers occasionally injure themselves by colliding with power cables or motor traffic. The National Grid is not an important problem for the species, since the Marsh Harrier does not habitually perch on pylons or cables and risk electrocution and it generally flies low enough to avoid cables. On migration or in travelling flight, however, there is a risk. I once saw a male Marsh Harrier almost collide with a cable whilst flying back to its nest (2 km away) with prey; he was heading straight for the wires and only at the last second suddenly dropped like a stone for several feet to avoid them, creditably not dropping the prey! Fox (1977b) reported a Swamp Harrier with only one wing, found at a New Zealand waterhole, presumed to be a victim of a wire strike or road accident; the stump was healed over and the bird was otherwise in good condition.

Legislation

In past times, the first legislation for birds of prey was a premium on their heads! In Britain, The Protection of Birds Act 1954 gave the Marsh Harrier and many other rare birds their first comprehensive legal protection. All species of harrier are now listed in Schedule 1, Part 1, of The Wildlife and Countryside Act 1981 (species which are protected by special penalties at all times and cannot intentionally be disturbed at the nest without a licence). Legislation is of course useless without enforcement. In Britain the RSPB takes on an investigative role in cases of poisoning and persecution.
Harriers kept in captivity must be registered with the Department of the Environment and ringed with a special numbered band supplied by the DoE. Only birds bred in captivity from parents kept lawfully in captivity can be sold, and only if registered and ringed with a DoE close ring.

On the international front, the Marsh Harrier is protected under Annex 1 of the European Union Council Birds Directive on the conservation of wild birds and Appendix II of the Bern Convention.

The effect of protective legislation in France seems to have been profound in allowing the species to stage a comeback in western and northern Europe. Legal protection was given to all birds of prey in 1972, prior to which they were routinely shot. This does not mean that some illegal shooting has not continued, but Marsh Harriers began to re-establish themselves in parts of France and the reduction in shooting of migrants moving through was the impetus required to assist the recovery from organochlorines throughout Europe.

In New Zealand, the Swamp Harrier remained for a period one of the three birds not protected by law. Its habit of feeding on sheep carrion earned it a reputation for killing lambs, but no instances of this have been found by recent studies (Carroll 1968; Baker-Gabb 1981). It was unpopular for damaging Rabbits in commercial traps, and predation on gamebirds was often cited, too, but Carroll found no evidence of the latter in 124 stomachs from dead harriers, other than three ducks. Acclimatization societies paid a bounty for their legs or bills, quotas were set and thousands were killed each year. There is one amazing story of a harrier surviving without feet (Sutton 1973): it was finally shot coming in to roost with a full crop of sheep carrion, but about one third of the tarsus had clearly been missing for some time and had healed over; the bird had presumably been stunned and deprived of its feet by a trapper who had discarded it as dead, and it had survived on carrion ever since. The Swamp Harrier has recently been added to the schedule of partially protected species in New Zealand. Although it is common and widely distributed, its population has declined owing to control of the Rabbit and loss of marshland habitat. One important communal roost site threatened with development was recently accorded reserve status after action by local ornithologists (Baker-Gabb and Fitzherbert 1989).

Education

Several organizations now concentrate on producing accurate information on raptors. In Britain, the Hawk and Owl Trust carries out conservation, research and educational projects on a range of birds of prey. The Raptor Research Foundation is based in the USA, but it has an international membership and holds meetings in Europe; its rôle is one of dissemination of information. The Fonds d'Intervention pour les Rapaces (FIR) operates widely in France, Belgium, Switzerland and elsewhere promoting raptor conservation. The World Working Group on Birds of Prey and Owls has an informational role, especially in encouraging the conservation of the world's more threatened raptors; it holds a World Conference on Birds of Prey every four or five years. Other specialist bird-of-prey centres are the Israel and Africa raptor information centres (IRIC and ARIC).

The opening-up of the former USSR into Russia and the Commonwealth of Independent States has revealed a vast information gap. The eastern end of Western Palearctic bird-distribution maps have tended to show continuous range for species such as the Marsh Harrier, which are probably widely distributed but on which there is a lack of any precise information. Russian ornithologists are beginning to organize themselves, an example being the 'Raptor-Link' newsletter published by Eugene Potapov from a base in the UK at Oxford, and they are beginning to assess the problems of pollution and habitat loss.

Bibliography

Albin, E., *A natural History of Birds*, London, 1738

Altenburg, W., Daan, S., Starkenberg, J. and Zijlstra, M., *Behaviour* 79 (1982) 272–312

Altenburg, W., Bruinenberg-Rinsma, J., Wildschut, P. and Zijlstra, M., *Ardea* 75 (1987) 213–20

Amadon, D., *Emu* 40 (1941) 365–84

Arroyo, B.E. and King, J.R., *Ostrich* (in press)

Arvidsson, L., *Var Fagelvarld* 39 (1980) 385–92

Axell, H.E. and Hosking, E., *Minsmere, Portrait of a Bird Reserve*, Hutchinson, London,1977

Baker-Gabb, D.J., *Notornis* 26 (1979) 325–9

Baker-Gabb, D.J., *Notornis* 28 (1981) 103–19

Baker-Gabb, D.J., *Corella* 7 (1983) 109–13

Baker-Gabb, D.J., *Aust. Wildl. Res.* 11 (1984) 517–32

Baker-Gabb, D.J. *Emu* 86 (1986) 71–81

Baker-Gabb, D.J. and Fitzherbert, K., 'An overview of raptor movements and wintering places in Australia and New Zealand' in Meyburg, B. and Chancellor, R. (eds) *Raptors in the Modern World. World Working Group on Birds of Prey and Owls*, Berlin, 1989

Bakker, D., *Limosa* 22 (1949) 321–3

Balfour, E. and Cadbury, C.J., *Ornis Scand* 10 (1979) 133–41

Bannerman, D.A. and Lodge, G.E., *The Birds of the British Isles* Vol. 5, Oliver & Boyd, Edinburgh, 1956

Barnard, P. and Simmons, R., *Ostrich* 57 (1986) 107–9

Barre, N. and Barau, A., *Oiseaux de la Réunion*, Imprimerie Arts Graphiques Modernes, St-Denis, Réunion, 1980

Bavoux, Chr., Burneleau, G., Nicolau-Guillaumet, P. and Pasquet, E., *Alauda* 56 (1988) 246–60

Bavoux, Chr., Burneleau, G., Leroux, A. and Nicolau-Guillaumet, P., *Alauda* 57 (1989) 247–62

Bavoux, Chr., Burneleau, G. Cuisin, J. and Nicolau-Guillaumet, P., *Alauda* 58 (1990) 221–31

Bavoux, Chr., Burneleau, G., Cuisin, J. and Nicolau-Guillaumet, P., *Alauda* 59 (1991) 248–55

Bavoux, Chr., Burneleau, G., Nicolau-Guillaumet, P. and Picard, M., *Alauda* 60 (1992) 149–58

Bavoux, Chr. Burneleau, G. Nicolau-Guillaumet, P and Picard, M., *Alauda* 61 (1993) 173–9

Baxter, E.V. and Rintoul, L.J., *The Birds of Scotland*, Oliver and Boyd, Edinburgh, 1953

Bengston, S-A., *Oologists' Record* 41 (1967) 23–8

Berg, W. and Stieffel, A., *Falke* 15 (1968) 82–5

Bergier, P., *Les Rapaces Diurnes du Maroc*, Annales du CEEP, 1987

Bernis, F., *La Migracion de las Aves an el Estrecho de Gibralter* Vol. 1, Madrid, 1980

Bibby, C.J. and Lunn, J., *Biological Conservation* 23 (1981) 167–86

Bijlsma, R.G.. *Sandgrouse* 5 (1983) 19–44

Bijlsma, R., *Ecologische Atlas van de Nederlandse Roofvogels*, Schuyt, Haarlem, 1993

Bildstein, K.L., *J. Field Orn.* 53 (1982) 7–14

Bildstein, K.L., *Raptor Research* 26 (1992) 115–23

Birds in Cornwall

Birds of Lancaster and District

Black, M.S., *Emu* 57 (1957) 54

Blanco, G., Herrera, M.A., Fargallo, J.A. and Cuevas, J.A., *Raptor Research* 27 (1993) 165–6

Bock, W.F., *J. Orn.* 119 (1978) 298–307

Bock, W.F., *J. Orn.* 120 (1979) 416–30

Booth, E.T., *Rough notes on the birds observed during 25 years' shooting and collecting in the British Isles*, 1881 to 1887

Borioni, M., *Rapaci sul Conero*, Parco del Conero, 1993

Brichambaut, J.P. de., *Alauda* 46 (1978) 271

British Birds European News

Brown, B. and Child, P., *Notornis* 22 (1975) 10–22

Brown, L. and Amadon, D., *Eagles, Hawks and Falcons of the World*, Country Life Books, Feltham, 1968

Buckland, S.T., Bell, M.V. and Picozzi, N., *The Birds of North-East Scotland*, North-East Scotland Bird Club, 1990

Burrell, H., *Emu* 10 (1910) 135

Buxton, A., *Transactions of the Norfolk and Norwich Naturalists' Society* 13 (1932–33) 311–24

Buxton, A., *Fisherman Naturalist*, Collins, London, 1946

Bylin, K., *Vår Fågelvärld* 40 (1981) 455–60

Calford, M.B., Wise, L.Z. and Petigrew, J.D., *J. Comp. Physiol A* 157 (1985) 149–60

Cambridgeshire Bird Report

Carroll A.L.K., *Notornis* 15 (1968) 23–7

Chapman, A.F., *Proceedings of the Dorset Natural History and Archaeological Society* 99 (1977) 84–96

Cheke, A.S., 'The ecology of the surviving native land birds of Réunion' in Diamond, A.W., *Studies of Mascarene Island Birds*, Cambridge University Press, 1987

Clark, J. and Eyre, J.A. (eds), *Birds of Hampshire*, Hampshire Ornithological Society, 1993

Clark, W.S., *British Birds* 80 (1987) 61–72

Clark, W.S. and Forsman, R., *Dutch Birding* 12 (1990) 181–5

Clarke, R. (ed), *Proceedings of the Hawk and Owl Trust International Conference on the Ecology and Conservation of Harriers* (in press a)

Clarke, R., *Journal of the Bombay Natural History Society* (in press b)

Clarke, R., Bourgonje, A. and Castelijns, H., *Ibis* 135 (1993) 424–31

Clegg, T.M., *British Birds* 54 (1961) 428–9

Clouet, M., *L'Oiseaux et RFO* 48 (1978) 95–106

Clunie, F., *Notornis* 27 (1980) 114

Coates, B.J., *The Birds of Papua New Guinea* Vol. 1, Dove, Alderney, Qld., Australia, 1985

Colling, A.W. and Brown, E.B., *British Birds* 39 (1946) 233–43

Cramp, S. and Simmons, K.E.L., (eds) *Birds of the Western Palearctic* Vol. 2, Oxford University Press, 1980

Cupper, J. and Cupper, L., *Hawks in Focus*, Mildura, Jacklin, 1981

Danko, Š., Diviš, T., Divorská, J., Dvorský, M., Chavko, J., Karaska, D., Kloubec, B., Kurka, P., Matušík, H., Peške, L., Schröpfer, l. and Vacék, R. *Buteo* 6 (1994) 1–89

Day, J., *RSPB Conservation Review* 2 (1978) 17–19

Doherty, P.A., *British Birds* 71 (1978) 307–8

Donald, C.H., *Journal of the Bombay Natural History Society* 16 (1905) 504–5

Dovrat, E., 'The Kefar Kassem migration survey, autumns 1977–1987: a brief summary', in Yekutiel, D. (ed), *Raptors in Israel*, IBCE, Eilat, 1991

Essex Bird Report

Evans, A.H., *Turner on Birds*, Cambridge University Press, 1903

Fenech, N., *Fatal Flight. The Maltese Obsession with Killing Birds*, Quiller, London, 1992

Fennell, J.F.M., *Notornis* 27 (1980) 404–5

Fernández, C., *Ardea* 80 (1992) 281–4

Fernández, C. and Azkona, P., *Raptor Research* 26 (1992) 257–9

Fernández, C. and Azkona, P. *J. Field Ornithol.* 65 (1994a) 109–114

Fernández, C. and Azkona, P., *Raptor Research* 28 (1994b) 23–26

Finlayson, C., *Birds of the Strait of Gibraltar*, Poyser, 1991

Fouquet, M. and Yesou, P., *British Birds* 84 (1991) 438

Forrest, H.E., *Vertebrate Fauna of North Wales*, 1907

Fox, N.C., *Notornis* 24 (1977a) 9–19

Fox, N.C., *Notornis* 24 (1977b) 74

Galushin, V., *WWGBP Newsletter* 14 (1991) 9–10

Gamauf, A., *Greifvogel in Osterreich*, Umweltbundesamt, Wien, 1991

Gamauf, A., *Einflusse der Landwirtschaft und des Tourismus auf das Raum-Zeit-System von Rohrweihen (Circus aeruginosus) im Bereich des Nationalparks "Neusiedlersee-Seewinkel"*, 1993

Gardner, T. and Gardner, P., *Journey* 5 (1984) 112–15

Génsbøl, B., *Birds of Prey of Britain and Europe*, Collins, London, 1986

Gibbons, D.W., Reid, J.B. and Chapman. R.A., *The New Atlas of Breeding Birds in Britain and Ireland: 1988–1991* Poyser, London, 1993

Giordano, A., *WWGBP Bulletin* 4 (1991) ' 239–50

Giraud-Audine, M. and Pineau, J., *Alauda* 42 (1974) 281–8

Glutz von Blotzheim, U.K., Bauer, M. and Bezzel, E., *Handbuch der Vogel Mitteleuropas* Band 4, Akademische Verlagsgesellschaft, Frankfurt, 1971

González, J.L., *El Aguilucho lagunero Circus aeruginosus (L., 1748) en España. Situacion, Biologia de la reproduccion, alimentacion y Conservacion*, Colecc. Tec., ICONA, Madrid, 1991

Grieve, A., *Naturalist* 102 (1977) 125–32

Grootjans, B. and Ouweneel, G., *Het Vogeljaar* (1990) 82–3

Gurney, J.H., *Ibis* 4 (New series) (1868) 460–71

Gurr, L., *Ibis* 110 (1968) 332–7

Hadrill, P., *Kent Bird Report* (1989) 106–9

Hafner, J.C. and Hafner, M.S., *Auk* 94 (1977) 293–303

Hamerstrom, F. 'A harrier population study', in: Hickey, J.J. (ed), *Peregrine Falcon Populations: their Biology and Decline*, Madison, NY, 1969

Harris, P., *Bird Life* 7 (1973) 35

Harrison, C., *The History of the Birds of Britain*, Collins, London, 1988

Hedley, L.A., *Notornis* 30 (1983) 23–8

Hildén, O. and Kalinainen, P., *Ornis Fennica* 43 (1966) 85–124

Hobbs, J.N., *Emu* 59 (1959) 87–8

Hollands, D., *Eagles Hawks and Falcons of Australia*, Nelson, Melbourne, 1984

Hosking, E., *British Birds* 37 (1943) 2–9

Hutchinson, C., *Birds in Ireland*, Poyser, Calton, 1989

Ilyichew, V. (ed), *Migrations of Birds of Eastern Europe and Northern Asia*, Nauka, Moscow, 1982

Image, B., *Norfolk Bird and Mammal Report 1987*, 405–8

Image, R.A., *Norfolk Bird and Mammal Report 1991*, 270–2

Jenyns, L., *Trans. Cambridge Philosophical Soc.* 1826

Jones, C.G., *Gabar* 4 (1989) 22–3

Jorgensen, H.E., *Dansk Orn. Foren. Tidsskr* 79 (1985) 89–102

Jorgensen, H.E., Bomholt, P., Bogelund, S. and Jensen, P., *Dansk Orn. Foren. Tidsskr* 76 (1982) 3–14

Kalaber, L., *WWGBP Bulletin* 2 (1985) 37–43

Kent Bird Report

Koeman, J.H., Vink, J.A.J. and Goeij, J.J.M., *Ardea* 57 (1969) 67–74

Kent Ornithological Society, *The Birds of Kent*, 1981

King, B., *British Birds* 54 (1961) 161

King, F., *British Birds* 71 (1978) 589–90

Kjellen, N., *Anser* 32 (1993) 105–25

Leroux, A.B.A., 'Drainage of wet meadows and birds in West Marshes of France', in Curtis, D.J., Bignal, E.M. and Curtis, M.A. (eds), *Birds and Pastoral Agriculture in Europe*, JNCC, 1991

Lincolnshire and South Humberside Bird Report

Looft, V. and Busche, G., *Vogelwelt Schleswig-Holsteins*, Greifvögel, Wachholtz, Neümunster, 1990

Lovegrove, R. Williams, G. and Williams, I., *Birds in Wales*, Poyser, London, 1994

Marchant, S. and Higgins, P.J. (eds), *Handbook of Australian, New Zealand and Antarctic Birds*, Vol. 2, Oxford University Press, Melbourne, 1993

Martelli, D. and Parodi, R., 'Falco di Palude Circus aeruginosus' in Brichetti, P. et al (eds), Fauna d'Italia XXIX, Aves (1992), Ed. Calderini, Bologna, 527–33

Mead, C.J., Bird Study 20 (1973) 259–86

Meinertzhagen, R., Ibis 98 (1956), 535

Meininger, P.L., Berrevoets, C.M. and Strucker, R.C.W., Watervogeltellingen in het Zuidelijk Deltagebied 1987–91, RIKZ, Den Haag, 1994

Mlikovský, J. and Stýblo, P., Ecology of the Svjatoj Nos Wetlands, Lake Baikal, Ninox, Prague, 1992

Montagu, G., Ornithological Dictionary or Alphabetic Synopsis of British Birds, White, London, 1802

Moore, D.R., Suffolk Birds 36 (1987) 76–9

Moreau, R.E., The Palearctic-African Bird Migration Systems, Academic Press, London and New York, 1972

Nankivov, D. Stoyanov, G., Kouzmanov, G. and Todorov, R., WWGBP Bulletin 4 (1991) 293–302

Newton, A. (ed), Ootheca Wolleyana: an illustrated catalogue of the collection of birds' eggs formed by the late John Wolley, Van Voorst, London,1864

Newton, I., Population Ecology of Raptors, Poyser, Berkhamsted, 1979

Newton, I. (ed), Birds of Prey, Merehurst, London, 1990

Nieboer, E., Geographical and ecological differentiation in the genus Circus (Unpubl. PhD thesis), University of Amsterdam, 1973

Norfolk Bird Report

Norfolk Bird and Mammal Report

Odsjo, T. and Sondell, J., Vår Fågelvärld 36 (1977) 152–60

Olsen, P.D. and Olsen, J., Emu 87 (1987) 59–62

Pain, D.J., Amiard-Triquet, C., Bavoux, C., Burneleau, G., Eon, L. and Nicolau-Guillaumet, P., Ibis 135 (1993) 379–86

Persson, T., Var Fagelvarld 30 (1971) 125–6

Pierce, R.J. and Maloney, R.F., Notornis 36 (1989) 1–12

Picozzi, N., Ornis Scand. 15 (1984) 1–10

Pinowski, J. and Ryszkowski, L., Ekol.

Polska B 7 (1961), 55–60

Redhead, R.E., Notornis 16 (1969) 262–84

Rheinwald, G. Atlas der Verbreitung und Häufigkeit der Brutvögel Deutschlands, DDA, Berlin, 1993

Rice, W.R., Auk 99 (1982) 403–13

Risberg, L., Sveriges Faglar, Stockholm, 1990

Ringing and Migration

Riviere, B.B., A History of the Birds of Norfolk, Witherby, London, 1930

Robertson, H.A., New Zeal. J. Zool. 7 (1980) 579–83

Ruffino, R., Atlas das Aves que nidificam em Portugal Continental 1989., CEMPA, 1989

Sach, G., Corax 2 (1967) 9–17

Saurola, P., Ornis Fennica 62 (1985) 64–72

Schipper, W.J.A., Gerfaut 63 (1973) 17–120

Schipper, W.J.A., Ardea 65 (1977) 53–72

Schipper, W.J.A., Ardea 66 (1979) 77–102

Schipper, W.J.A., Buurma, L.S. and Bossenbroek, P.H., Ardea 63 (1975) 1–29

Selby, P.J., Illustrations of British Ornithology, Lizars, Edinburgh, 1825

Sharland, M.S., Emu 32 (1932) 87–90

Sharland, M.S., Emu 47 (1947) 81

Sharland, M.S., Emu 58 (1958) 75–80

Sharrock, J.T.R., The Atlas of Breeding Birds in Britain and Ireland, Poyser, Berkhamsted,1976

Shirihai, H. and Christie, D.A., British Birds 85 (1992) 141–86

Sibley, C.G. and Alquist, J.E., Phylogeney and Classification of Birds, a study in mollecular evolution, Yale University Press, New Haven, 1991

Sibley, C.G. and Monroe, B.L., Distribution and Taxonomy of Birds of the World, Yale University Press, New Haven, 1990

Sills, N., Marsh Harriers at Titchwell Marsh Reserve, Norfolk Bird and Mammal Report 1993 (342–8) and 1994 (84–95)

Sills, N., Titchwell Marsh. The first ten years, RSPB, 1983

Sills, N., RSPB Conservation Review 1988, 64–8

Simmons, R., Auk 105 (1988a) 303–7

Simmons, R., Gabar 13 (1988b) 35–7

Simmons, R., 'How polygynous female Northern Harriers *Circus cyaneus* choose their mates and why they are deceived' in Meyburg, B.–U. and Chancellor, R.D. (eds), *Raptors in the Modern World*, WWGBP, Berlin, 1989

Simmons, R., *Anim. Behav.* 40 (1990) 1151–57

Simmons, R., *Ostrich* 62 (1991a) 45–51

Simmons, R., *Gabar* 6 (2) (1991b) 51–6

Somerset Birds

Sondell, J., *Var Fagelvarld* 29 (1970) 288–99

Stead, E.F., *Life Histories of New Zealand Birds*, Search, London, 1932

Suetens, W., *Les Rapaces d'Europe*, Perron, 1989

Suffolk Birds

Sutton, R.R., *Notornis* 20 (1973) 74

Thevenot, M., Bergier, P. and Beaubrun, P., 'Present distribution and status of raptors in Morocco' in Newton, I. and Chancellor, R.D. (eds), *Conservation Studies on Raptors*, ICBP, 1985

Thiollay, J. -M., *Nos Oiseaux* 30 (1970), 214–29

Thomsen, P. and Jacobsen, P., *The Birds of Tunisia*, Copenhagen, 1979

Thornett, R., *Devon Birds* 4 (1) (1991) 13–19

Ticehurst, C.B., *The Birds of Suffolk*, London, 1932

Tomialojc, L., *WWGBP Newsletter* 13 (1990) 1–2

Tollan, A.M., *Ardea* 76 (1988) 181–6

Tsovel, A. and Allon, D., 'Soaring bird migration surveys in the northern valleys of Israel – autumns 1988–1990' in Yekutiel, D., *Raptors in Israel*, IBCE, Eilat, 1991

Underhill-Day, J.C., *J. Appl. Ecol.* 21 (1984) 773–87

Underhill-Day, J.C., *Bird Study* 32 (1985) 199–206

Underhill-Day, J.C., *Ardea* 77 (1989) 47–55

Vasic, V., Grubac, B., Susic, G. and Marinkovic, S., *The status of birds of prey in Yugoslavia, with particular reference to Macedonia* in Newton, I. and Chancellor, R.D. (eds), *Conservation Studies on Raptors*, ICBP, 1985

Vaurie, C., *The Birds of the Palearctic Fauna*, Witherby, London, 1965

Vestjens, W.J.M., *Emu* 72 (1972) 115

Vincent, J., 'The Marsh and Hen-harriers' in Pitt, F. (ed), *The Romance of Nature* Country Life

Weis, H., *Life of the Harrier in Denmark*, Wheldon and Wesley, London, 1923

Welch, G.R. and Welch, H.J., *Sandgrouse* 10 (1988) 26–50

Wheeldon, R.E., *Falconer* 7 (1981) 317–18

Wheeldon, R., *Hawk Chalk* 31 (1992) 53–5

Wild Bird Protection in Norfolk

Williams, J.L.R., *Raptor* 22 (1995) 24–6

Witherby, H.F., *Ibis* 4, 12th series (1928) 587–663

Witherby, H.F., Jourdain, F.C.R., Ticehurst, N.E. and Tucker, B.W., *The Handbook of British Birds* Vol 3, Witherby, London, 1940

Witkowski, J., *Acta Orn.* 25 (1989) 223–320

Woets, D., *Het Vogeljaar* 34 (1986) 257–70

Woets, D., *Het Vogeljaar* 37 (1989) 19

Yeatman-Berthelot, D., *Atlas des Oiseaux de France en Hiver*, Société Ornithologique de France, 1991

Yorkshire Bird Report

Zang, H., Heckenroth, H. and Knolle, F., *Die Vögel Niedersachsens - Greifvogel*, Naturschutz und Landschaftspflege in Niedersachsen, Hannover, 1989

Zijlstra, M., *Limosa* 60 (1987) 57-62

Zuppke, U., *Zool. Abh.* (Dres) 42 (14) (1987) 169-80

Scientific Names

BIRDS
Great Crested Grebe *Podiceps cristatus*
Manx Shearwater *Puffinus puffinus*
Little Cormorant *Phalacrocorax niger*
Australian Darter *Anhinga novaehollandiae*
Bittern *Botaurus stellaris*
Purple Heron *Ardea purpurea*
Spoonbill *Platalea leucorodia*
Wigeon *Anas penelope*
(Common) Teal *Anas crecca*
Mallard *A. platyrhynchos*
Pintail *A. acuta*
Garganey *A. querquedula*
Pochard *Aythya ferina*
California Condor *Gymnogyps californianus*
Honey Buzzard *Pernis apivorus*
Black Kite *Milvus migrans*
Red Kite *M. milvus*
Whistling Kite *Haliastur sphenurus*
White-tailed Eagle *Haliaeetus. albicilla*
Spotted Harrier *Circus assimilis*
Marsh Harrier *C. aeruginosus*
Eastern Marsh Harrier *C. spilonotus spilonotus*
Papuan Harrier *C. spilonotus spilothorax*
Réunion Harrier *C. maillardi maillardi*
Madagascar harrier *C. maillardi macrosceles*
Swamp Harrier *C. approximans*
African Marsh Harrier *C. ranivorus*
Black Harrier *C. maurus*
Hen Harrier *C. cyaneus*
Northern Harrier *C. hudsonius*
Cinereous Harrier *C. cinereus*
Pallid Harrier *C. macrourus*
Montagu's Harrier *C. pygargus*
Pied Harrier *C. melanoleucos*
Long-winged Harrier *C. buffoni*
Goshawk *Accipiter gentilis*
Sparrowhawk *A. nisus*
Brown Goshawk *A. fasciatus*
(Common) Buzzard *Buteo buteo*
Booted Eagle *Hieraaetus pennatus*
Osprey *Pandion haliaetus*
Kestrel *Falco tinnunculus*
Brown Falcon *F. berigora*
New Zealand Falcon *F. novaezeelandiae*
Peregrine Falcon *F. peregrinus*
Red-legged Partridge *Alectoris rufa*

Grey Partridge *Perdix perdix*
Pheasant *Phasianus colchicus*
Water Rail *Rallus aquaticus*
Moorhen *Gallinula chloropus*
Coot *Fulica atra*
Common Crane *Grus grus*
Lapwing *Vanellus vanellus*
Snipe *Gallinago gallinago*
Redshank *Tringa totanus*
Black-headed Gull *Larus ridibundus*
Kelp Gull *L. dominicanus*
Barn Owl *Tyto alba*
Short-eared Owl *Asio flammeus*
Skylark *Alauda arvensis*
Meadow Pipit *Anthus pratensis*
Blackbird *Turdus merula*
Reed Warbler *Acrocephalus scirpaceus*
Bearded Tit *Panurus biarmicus*
Little Raven *Corvus mellori*
Starling *Sturnus vulgaris*
Yellowhammer *Emberiza citrinella*

MAMMALS
Hedgehog *Erinaceus* spp.
Mole *Talpa europaea*
Rabbit *Oryctolagus cuniculus*
Hare *Lepus* spp.
Coypu *Myocaster coypus*
Field Vole *Microtus agrestis*
Common Vole *M. arvalis*
Water Vole *Arvicola terrestris*
Muskrat *Ondatra zibethicus*
Rat *Rattus* spp.
Harvest Mouse *Micromys minutus*
Wolf *Canis lupus*
Jackal *C. aureus*
Fox *Vulpes vulpes*
Desert Fox *V. vulges puisilla*
Indian Fox *V. bengalensis*
Stoat *Mustela erminea*
Weasel *M. nivalis*
(European) Mink *M. lutreola*
(American) Mink *M. vison*
Polecat *M. putorius*
Marten *Martes* spp.
Wild Boar *Sus scrofa*

Index

NATURAL HISTORY BOOKS

A complete range of Hamlyn Natural History titles is available from all good bookshops or by mail order direct from the publisher. Payment can be made by credit card or cheque/postal order in the following ways:

BY PHONE
Phone through your order on our special *Credit Card Hotline* on **01933 414 000**. Speak to our customer service team during office hours (9 a.m. to 5 p.m.) or leave a message on the answer machine, quoting your full credit card number plus expiry date and your full name and address. Please also quote the reference number J508N12C.

BY POST
Simply fill out the order form below (photocopies are acceptable) and send it with your payment to:
Cash Sales Department,
Reed Book Services Ltd.,
P.O. Box 5,
Rushden,
Northants, NN10 6YX

J508N12C

I wish to order the following titles:

	ISBN	Price	Quantity Total
Hamlyn Guide to the Birds of Britain and Europe	0 600 57492 X	£8.99	.... £.......
Photographic Guide to Birds of Britain and Europe	0 600 57861 5	£9.99	.... £.......
Where to Watch Birds in Britain and Europe	0 600 58007 5	£12.99	.... £.......
Hamlyn Species Guide: The Kestrel	0 540 01278 5	£12.99	.... £.......
Hamlyn Species Guide: The Barn Owl	0 600 57949 2	£12.99	.... £.......

Add £2.00 for postage and packing if your order is worth £10.00 or less £.......

Grand Total £.......

Name _____ (block capitals)

Address _____

_____ Postcode _____

I enclose a cheque/postal order for £ _____ made payable to Reed Book Services Ltd
or
Please debit my ☐ Access   ☐ Visa   ☐ American Express   ☐ Diners

account number ☐☐☐☐ ☐☐☐☐ ☐☐☐☐ ☐☐☐☐

by £ _____ Expiry date _____ Signature _____

SPECIAL OFFER: FREE POSTAGE AND PACKAGING FOR ALL ORDERS OVER £10.00, add £2.00 for p+p if your order is £10.00 or less.

Whilst every effort is made to keep our prices low, the publisher reserves the right to increase the prices at short notice.
Your order will be dispatched within 5 days, but please allow up to 28 days for delivery, subject to availability.
Registered office: Michelin House, 81 Fulham Road, London SW3 6RB.
Registered in England no 1974080.

If you do not wish your name to be used by other carefully selected organizations for promotional purposes, please tick this box ☐